THE ILLUSTRATORS 1

www.chrisbeetles.com

C000264488

No.	Price	No.	Price	No.	Price	No.	Price	No.	Price
1	12500	35	3500	69	1450	10?		137	9500
2	45000	36	3500	70	4250	104	2750	138	2750
3	45000	37	4500	71	4500	105	1750	139	7500
4	55000	38	3500	72	2450	106	1250	140	4500
5	850	39	7500	73	2750	107	3500	141	6500
6	850	40	4500	74	950	108	1750	142	6500
7	2750	41	1750	75	2750	109	4500	143	5500
8	4500	42	2250	76	1850	110	7500	144	3750
9	8500	43	4500	77	450	111	1750	145	1450
10	4500	44	4500	78	1750	112	9500	146	1750
11	3500	45	6500	79	650	113	6500	147	1450
12	6500	46	3250	80	1450	114	4500	148	1450
13	7500	47	4500	81	750	115	12500	149	1450
14	750	48	4250	82	850	116	12500	150	3500
15	375	49	4250	83	850	117	4500	151	3500
16	400	50	5500	84	750	118	12500	152	3500
17	9500	51	3750	85	650	119	9500	153	3500
18	9500	52	5500	86	850	120	9500	154	3500
19	850	53	5500	87	650	121	8500	155	4000
20	1250	54	4500	88	650	122	4500	156	3500
21	1750	55	2750	89	850	123	8500	157	3250
22	4500	56	2250	90	650	124	2750	158	2250
23	12500	57	1850	91	650	125	3500	159	2250
24	12500	58	1750	92	850	126	4500	160	2750
25	8500	59	1750	93	650	127	4500	161	2750
26	8500	60	850	94	650	128	6500	162	3500
27	1450	61	1750	95	2750	129	4500	163	2750
28	12500	62	950	96	4500	130	8500	164	2750
29	4500	63	950	97	3750	131	3250	165	2250
30	2750	64	1450	98	3500	132	ON LOAN	166	1450
31	3500	65	ON LOAN	99	750	133	2450	167	950
32	3500	66	45000	100	3750	134	4500	168	1250
33	4500	67	3750	101	2750	135	7500	169	950
34	4500	68	2750	102	4500	136	7500	170	950

171	1250	207	1450	243	1450	279	600
172	650	208	1250	244	2250	280	750
173	650	209	450	245	1750	281	750
174	650	210	1750	246	2250	282	750
175	650	211	1750	247	1450	283	550
176	850	212	350	248	450	284	750
177	750	213	1750	249	650	285	1450
178	750	214	1450	250	750	286	1450
179	750	215	2750	251	750	287	1450
180	750	216	2750	252	750	288	1450
181	750	217	3500	253	650	289	1450
182	750	218	1450	254	450	290	1450
183	750	219	950	255	650	291	350
184	1250	220	1450	256	750	292	350
185	1250	221	1450	257	750	293	350
186	1250	222	1450	258	750	294	350
187	1250	223	17500	259	1250	295	350
188	6500	224	1250	260	650	296	350
189	2750	225	2750	261	650	297	350
190	1750	226	850	262	950	298	350
191	3500	227	850	263	750	299	350
192	3500	228	2750	264	550	300	350
193	950	229	450	265	1250	301	350
194	2750	230	550	266	850		
195	2750	231	550	267	750		
196	3500	232	750	268	750		
197	3500	233	450	269	850		
198	6500	234	750	270	3500		
199	1250	235	850	271	1750		
200	1450	236	1450	272	850		
201	2750	237	750	273	850		
202	3500	238	1450	274	2750		
203	1250	239	1750	275	750		
204	2250	240	850	276	1750		
205	2750	241	850	277	650		
206	1450	242	2250	278	550		

www.chrisbeetles.com

To the great Arnold Roth,
our favourite All American Boy

Copyright © Chris Beetles Ltd 2020
8 & 10 Ryder Street
St James's
London SW1Y 6QB
020 7839 7551
gallery@chrisbeetles.com
www.chrisbeetles.com

ISBN 978-1-905738-98-4

Cataloguing in publication data is available
from the British Library

Researched and written by David Wootton,
with contributions from Alexander Beetles, Chris Beetles,
Michael Foreman and Anne Stevenson Hobbs

Edited by Alexander Beetles, Fiona Nickerson,
Pascale Oakley and David Wootton

Design by Fiona Nickerson and Pascale Oakley

Photography by Julian Huxley-Parlour
Reproduction by www.cast2create.com
Colour separation and printing by Geoff Neal Litho Limited

Front cover:
Arnold Roth, *Our Cottontail Cornucopia Runneth Over* [198]

Front endpaper:
Thomas Mackenzie, *Scheherazade Dancing* [10]

This page:
Lawson Wood, *Monkey Band* [detail of 34]

Title page:
Edward Ardizzone, *Tim to the Rescue* [detail of 112]

Back endpaper:
Michael Foreman, *'This is the life', he thought. 'I am king on my very own castle.'* [205]

Back cover:
Beatrix Potter, *Squirrel with a Hazelnut* [3]

THE ILLUSTRATORS
THE BRITISH ART OF ILLUSTRATION 1894-2020

CHRIS BEETLES

8 & 10 Ryder Street, St James's, London SW1Y 6QB
020 7839 7551 gallery@chrisbeetles.com
www.chrisbeetles.com

CONTENTS

1 Fairy & Fantasy

ARTHUR RACKHAM

Arthur Rackham, VPRWS (1867-1939)

If the major gift book illustrators were to divide the world between them, Arthur Rackham would claim the northern lands. His early familiarity with the English countryside was soon matched by a fascination with Germany, stimulated by walking tours. The knowledge that he gleaned from these travels gave him the authority to represent touchstones of Romanticism, from Andersen to Wagner, in uncanny detail. His vision is so comprehensive and so convincing that it seems we need look just a little harder; if we do, we too would see Shakespeare's fairies playing in the hedgerows and Grimm's goblins looming out from the shadows cast by twisted trees.

For a biography of Arthur Rackham, please refer to *The Illustrators*, 2018, page 4.

1 (opposite)
THERE BROKE FORTH A WAILING AND A LAMENTATION
Signed and dated 1904
Pen ink and watercolour
15 ¼ x 11 inches
Provenance: Luke Gertler
Illustrated: *Little Folks Magazine*, October 1901, 'Stories of the Edda; of The Gods of Asgard: IX – The Death of Balder' by E S Buchheim (in black and white);
The Land of Enchantment, London: Cassell and Company, 1907, Page 137, 'Stories from the Edda: IX – The Death of Balder' by E S Buchheim (in black and white)
Arthur Rackham reworked the drawing between its appearances in *Little Folks* and *The Land of Enchantment*, and subsequently coloured it.

There broke forth a wailing and a lamentation

Between 1896 and 1905, Arthur Rackham regularly illustrated stories that appeared in *Little Folks*, a 'magazine for the young' edited by his friend, Sam Hamer. In 1907, the magazine's publisher, Cassell, collected together five of these stories, with their illustrations, in the volume, *The Land of Enchantment*. One the five, 'Stories from the Edda', was itself a collection of eleven Norse myths retold by Emma Sophia Buchheim (1860-1951), a writer, translator and lecturer in German at King's College, London. Her retellings were based on two Icelandic literary works, the Prose Edda and the Poetic Edda, both written down in the thirteenth century.

The present work illustrates the ninth of the 'Stories from the Edda', entitled 'The Death of Balder'. The gods were afraid for the safety of Balder the Beloved, one of their number and the son of Odin and Frigg. Frigg took an oath from all things living and dead that no harm should come to him. The Gods then considered him so safe that it became their sport to throw weapons at him. However, one god, Loki, who was envious of Balder, discovered that Frigg had asked no oath from mistletoe, because it seemed so insignificant. So he obtained the mistletoe and gave it to Hœder, who, blind and weaponless, had not joined in the sport. Under Loki's direction, Hœder threw the plant, pierced Balder's skin and killed him. Rackham's illustration captures the immediate response to his death, as the gods begin to lament.

Balder's brother, Hermodhr, followed his body to the underworld. On arrival, he pleaded with Hel, the presiding goddess, to let Balder return with him, because the whole world was grieving. She agreed to let him go, on condition that all things on earth, both living and dead, wept for him. Unfortunately, a giantess named Thœck (believed by some to be Loki in disguise) refused to do so, saying that 'Little good had I from him, living or dead'. So Balder remained with Hel. The unwitting murderer, Hœder, was killed by Vali, another of Balder's brothers, while Loki was permanently bound to three upright stones. The death of Balder is considered the first in a chain of events that leads to Ragnarok, the twilight of the gods.

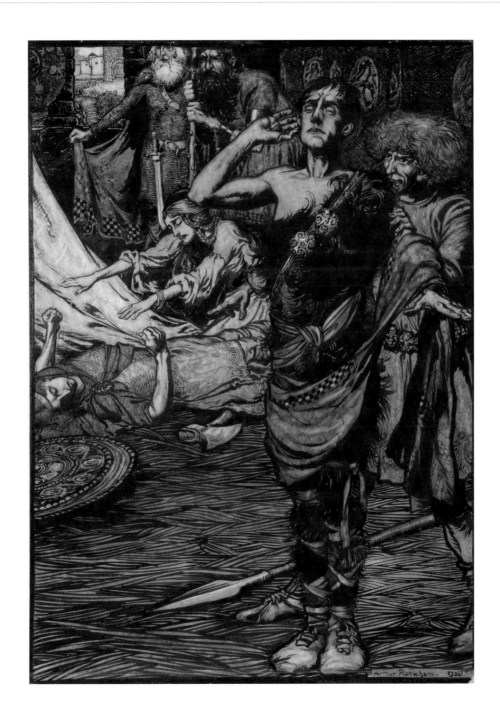

2
PETER SCREAMED OUT
'DO IT AGAIN', AND
WITH GREAT GOOD
NATURE THEY DID IT
SEVERAL TIMES
Signed and dated 06
Pen ink and watercolour
10 ½ x 7 ½ inches
Illustrated: J M Barrie, *Peter Pan in Kensington Gardens*, London: Hodder and Stoughton, 1906
Exhibited: 'Drawing on Childhood', The Foundling Museum, London, January-May 2016;
'Les drôles de petites bêtes d'Antoon Krings', Musée des Arts Decoratifs, Paris, April-September 2019

BEATRIX POTTER
Helen Beatrix Potter (1866-1943)

Beatrix Potter's picture books remain a landmark in the history of the genre. Originally published in a variety of forms, each volume had its appearance tailored to a particular text, and the integration of word and image was carefully considered. Though Potter made use of a basic anthropomorphism, she tended to eschew further fantasy, and the great success of her illustration often lies in the sense it gives of a particular place.

Beatrix Potter was born at 2 Bolton Gardens, South Kensington, London, on 28 July 1866, the elder child and only daughter of a barrister who chose to live as a dilettante, with painting and photography numbered among his interests. Beatrix herself led a very sheltered life for many years, remaining with her parents until she was nearly 40. Educated at home, she was entirely self-taught as an artist. She sketched fungi, fossils and fabrics in the South Kensington Museums, and animals, both furtively at home, and during family summer holidays in the Lake District and Scotland. Then developing an interest in illustration, she absorbed the influence of Thomas Bewick, Randolph Caldecott, Walter Crane and John Tenniel, as she published some greetings' cards and a first book, *The Happy Pair* (both 1890). Three years later, she invented the character of Peter Rabbit in a series of picture-letters for Noel Moore, the son of her former companion, Annie Carter. These formed the basis of *The Tale of Peter Rabbit*, which was privately printed in 1900, and finally accepted by Frederick Warne & Co two years later. This was followed by several more of her classic tales.

After a fierce battle with her parents, in 1905, Potter became engaged to Norman Warne, her editor, though two years later he died. Soon after, she bought Hill Top Farm at Sawrey, near Windermere, gaining a measure of independence and becoming a capable farmer. During the following eight years she produced much of her best work, and both her home and the adjacent Castle Farm, which she bought in 1909, were used as the settings for at least six of her books. Originally published in a variety of forms, each volume had its appearance tailored to a particular text, and the integration of word and image was carefully considered. Though Potter made use of a basic anthropomorphism, she tended to eschew further fantasy, and the great success of her illustration often lies in the sense it gives of a particular place.

Following her marriage to William Heelis, an Appleby solicitor, in 1913, Potter worked little as an illustrator and spent much of her time farming. She died at Hill Top Farm on 22 December 1943. Her properties were bequeathed to the National Trust.

Her work is represented in numerous public collections, including the British Museum, Tate and the V&A.

Further reading

Margit Sperling Cotsen, *The Beatrix Potter collection of Lloyd Cotsen*, Los Angeles: Cotsen Occasional Press, 2004;
Anne Stevenson Hobbs, *Beatrix Potter: artist and illustrator*, London: Frederick Warne, 2005;
Anne Stevenson Hobbs (compiler), *The Linder Collection of the watercolours and drawings of Beatrix Potter*, [London]: Trustees of the Linder Collection, 1996;
Anne Stevenson Hobbs and Joyce Irene Whalley (compilers), *Beatrix Potter: the V&A Collection*. The Leslie Linder Bequest, London: V&A Museum/Warne, 1985;
Margaret Lane, *The Tale of Beatrix Potter*, London: Warne, 1946;
Leslie Linder, *A history of the writings of Beatrix Potter*, London: Warne, 1987 (revised reprint);
Leslie Linder (transcriber), *The Journal of Beatrix Potter, 1881-1897*, Harmondsworth: Warne, 1989 (new revised edition);
Anne Carroll Moore, *The Art of Beatrix Potter*, London: Warne, 1955;
Lolly Robinson, 'Beatrix Potter's illustration styles as seen in Appley Dapply's Nursery Rhymes', *The Picture Book*, 20 December 1987;
V A J Slowe, 'Potter, Helen Beatrix (*b* London, 28 July 1866; *d* Near Sawrey, Cumbria, 22 Dec 1943)', Jane Turner (ed), *The Dictionary of Art*, London: Macmillan, 1996, vol 25, page 372;
Judy Taylor, *Beatrix Potter, artist, storyteller and countrywoman*, London: Warne, 1986;
Judy Taylor (collected & introduced), *Letters to children from Beatrix Potter*, London: Warne, 1997;
Judy Taylor, 'Potter [married name Heelis], (Helen) Beatrix (1866-1943)', H C G Matthew and Brian Harrison (eds), *Oxford Dictionary of National Biography*, Oxford University Press, 2004, vol 45, pages 10-11

The notes on the works by Beatrix Potter are written by Anne Stevenson Hobbs, the foremost expert on Potter's work, and a great-niece of Arthur Rackham.

She has written extensively on illustration and children's literature, and especially the work of Beatrix Potter (including titles listed here in Further Reading). She was formerly a curator at the British Museum (1964-66) and the Victoria & Albert Museum (1966-2002, including curator of special collections at the National Art Library and Frederick Warne Curator of Children's Literature). Also a violinist and pianist, she was one of the founder members of the Mantegazza String Quartet.

Squirrel with a Hazelnut

Squirrels are much rarer players than mice in Beatrix Potter's fantasy works, although she often drew them for children in picture letters. Occasionally she lets them engage in quasi-human activities, but rarely treats them anthropomorphically. They are never clothed. She preferred to draw them as wild creatures in their native surroundings, among tree branches or as small figures in a woodland glade. This striking squirrel is not Nutkin but a predecessor, drawn in a more schematic setting and momentarily still: seemingly a very different character from the familiar impudent and hyperactive hero of her celebrated Tale.

On 8 August 1896, holidaying with Mr and Mrs Potter in Sawrey, Beatrix visited her Gaddum cousins at Sawrey Knotts on Windermere. That same day she wrote to young Eric Moore, 'my little cousin Molly Gaddum has a squirrel and two babies', and drew them for him. She refers to this visit in a letter sent from London on 6 March 1897 to four-year-old Molly's brother Walter, then aged seven, showing a crouching squirrel, facing to the left and holding a nut. She had already sent Walter several ingenious movable 'toy pictures', now in the V&A and Cotsen Collections; Molly however was given the original tale of a fishing frog. Six years later another nut-eating squirrel, enclosed in a circular frame but now reversed to face right again, decorates the title page of *The Tale of Squirrel Nutkin*.

In Perthshire Beatrix Potter observed a squirrel trying to catch sparrows: 'its fierce little excited movements reminded me of a monkey' (*Journal*, 21 August 1892). Writing on the same day to Eric Moore from Birnam, she records a Nutkin-like squirrel several generations older than Nutkin himself, but he was born among the red squirrel colonies of Cumberland. Between 1897 and 1907 the Potters stayed no fewer than seven times, in late summer and autumn, on the shores of Derwentwater – and here the seeds of a new story were sown. The hero makes his first appearance in an illustrated letter sent to Norah Moore from Lingholm on 25 September 1901. Beatrix had seen a tail-less squirrel: 'he was so impertinent, chattering and clattering and throwing down acorns onto my head'; most unusually, she includes herself in her drawing of this little drama. The new Tale had a long gestation: landscape sketches were done in late Summer 1901, and drawings for the book begun in December 1902. Live models had to be bought from a London pet shop, since her cousins' gamekeeper

at Melford Hall could not get a squirrel (letter to Norman Warne, 22 November 1902). *The Tale of Squirrel Nutkin* was published at last in August 1903, supplanting a planned nursery rhyme book. Its illustrations include some of the artist's most characteristic and charming images.

Beatrix Potter tried out different styles and techniques from early in her career; as she experimented, so her confidence grew. The greetings card designs, the picture stories and the rhyme sequences produced from 1890 onwards are executed with a miniaturist's fine dry brush, and most of the line drawings too are drawn with a fine nib. Her animal studies, both scientific and imaginary, vary in size as well as technique. Squirrels were difficult models, volatile and hyperactive: such a fast-moving creature had to be captured in pencil impressions or in rapid washes. She filled whole sketchbooks with squirrels; other studies include the 'head of a dead specimen', an experiment in grey wash. There were also experiments in 'grisaille': fine stippled lines in grey wash heightened with white, as in *The Squirrel's Gift*. A matched pair of designs shows two squirrels on a log; they fit together perfectly to make a shaped greetings card. Squirrel anatomy, with its supple, serpentine form, lent itself to designs for borders, an endpaper design, and layouts for menu cards (all unfinished).

Beatrix Potter's subjects are individuals, but their individuality is especially striking in the larger-scale images, whether fantasy subjects such as *The Rabbits' Christmas Party* or straightforwardly scientific studies 'from nature'. (Even the fungi have personality.) For such portraits, relatively rare among her work, she chose a brighter palette, as in two striking parrot studies at the Free Library of Philadelphia. A pointillistic owl painted in a surprising range of tints is not Old Mr Brown but her brother's pet owl from the mid-1890s. We know of only one mouse picture (from 1896) drawn in a technique similar to that found in the Gaddum squirrel, using a broader brush and looser brushstrokes.

This squirrel is almost certainly little Molly Gaddum's pet, 'Mrs. Frisky'. The artist has succeeded in conveying its large lustrous eye, the feathery texture of its coat, and the soft downy texture of the hazel leaves among which it sits alert and wary, pausing for a moment as it feasts.

3 (opposite)
SQUIRREL WITH A HAZELNUT
Watercolour with bodycolour and pencil
9 ¼ x 5 ½ inches
Provenance: The descendants of Walter and Margery (Molly) Gaddum,
the children of Edith Gaddum, Beatrix Potter's cousin;

There was an old Woman.
Who lived in a Shoe,
She had so many Children
She did n't know what To do!

She gave them some Broth
Without any Bread –
She whipped them all round –

And put them to Bed!

There was an old woman who lived in a shoe

From an early age Beatrix Potter was fascinated by folklore: fairy tales, fables and traditional rhymes. Writing to her publisher in July 1902, she suggested a book of nursery rhymes in the style of 'Caldecott and *The Baby's Opera*', but an original story won the day (*The Tale of Squirrel Nutkin* appeared in August 1903). Planned for 1905 instead, the rhyme book was delayed by the death of her fiancé, Norman Warne. It survives in the National Trust collection as a manuscript dummy, the '1905 Book of Rhymes'. Rough sketches, some coloured and most with framed borders, accompany a collection of over 30 rhymes; all but one have animal protagonists.

According to *The Oxford Dictionary of Nursery Rhymes*, the celebrated inhabitant of a shoe 'has been identified with several ladies', probably because they had large families; the authors discreetly refer to the symbolism of the shoe. 'The Old Woman who lived in a Shoe' is an ancient rhyme, surviving in a variety of texts, more or less crude. Beatrix Potter's verses veer from the one most familiar today (used here) to her own cosier adaptation for *Appley Dapply's Nursery Rhymes* in 1917, 'You know the old woman who lived in a shoe?'. It ends 'I think if she lived in a little shoe-house – /That little old woman was surely a mouse!'

This three-page rhyme sequence comprises six of eight lines (in Beatrix Potter's hand) and three pictures: a running mouse; a mother mouse with babies and cradle; and a white mouse lying in bed. Mice proliferate in most of Beatrix Potter's early rhyme pictures, often charmingly clothed but still mouse-like. She became especially fond of mice. 'I shall be glad to get done

with the rabbits', she declared in a letter to Norman Warne (18 February 1904). On the first page are five lines of the rhyme in manuscript; on the second page is the last line of the second verse; and the third page has no text at all.

Best-known of the three images is the second one, of which at least eight variants are known. Here the mother mouse sits in a rocking chair, nursing a mouse baby as she rocks with her foot a wooden cradle containing two more young mice. This scene was re-drawn for the picture of Hunca Munca and her family in *The Tale of Two Bad Mice* (1904), where four little mice are crammed into a wicker cradle from the doll's house: 'Hunca Munca has got the cradle, and some of Lucinda's clothes'. The design was redrawn much larger and in heavy black ink for *Peter Rabbit's Painting Book* (1911).

Animals tucked up in bed, sick or sleeping, were a favourite subject. The first known ailing mouse (but surely this is a rat?) was drawn in August 1892, during a stay in Perthshire. The attendant physician was Dr Culbard of Birnam, caricatured as a mole; the mouse was Mrs Potter. Also at Birnam, Beatrix had been giving medicine to a very ill mouse (21 August 1892). In a letter to Noel Moore (8 March 1895) we find another mouse-patient, cared for by Mr Mole and Nurse Mouse with a tea-cup. By 1901 (26 October) the brass bed has become a four poster at Melford Hall – and the mouse is Beatrix.

From about 1890 Beatrix Potter produced a number of illustrated sequences, captioned or wordless. Most were devised as gifts, but some were done for profit. As so often with her designs, the original image

4

THERE WAS AN OLD WOMAN
WHO LIVED IN A SHOE,
SHE HAD SO MANY CHILDREN
SHE DIDN'T KNOW WHAT TO DO!
SHE GAVE THEM SOME BROTH
WITHOUT ANY BREAD –
SHE WHIPPED THEM ALL AROUND –
AND PUT THEM TO BED!

Inscribed with title
Pen ink and watercolour
Three images measuring 4 x 6 ½, 4 x 6 ½, and 4 x 5 ½ inches
Exhibited: 'The Long Nineteenth Century: Treasures and Pleasures',
Chris Beetles Gallery, March-April 2014, No 161
Drawn about 1917

The three images
shown mounted

inspires a number of variants; one is a two-page version presented to her cousin Caroline Hutton for Christmas 1897. There are extra images in the dummy 'Book of Rhymes', as also in the most complete sequence yet known: five sheets dated February 1897 (Linder Bequest, V&A Museum); here too the last scene is an image without text. The National Trust and V&A versions both illustrate 'She whipped them all round', not included in *Appley Dapply's Nursery Rhymes*.

By 1917 Beatrix Potter's publishers were in trouble and desperately needed a new story – but she insisted on a rhyme book. It is a 'patchwork' of old and new, compiled in a hurry. Of the seven rhymes selected, nearly all are original and only the 'Old Woman in a Shoe', fourth in the book, is a traditional nursery rhyme. It has two illustrations: the mice in a shoe, and (to accompany the end of the rhyme, when the children are in bed) a peacefully knitting mouse. This design was originally intended for a cover; it

belongs to an unpublished knitting rhyme, and is not included in any of her earlier versions of 'The Old Woman who lived in a Shoe'.

Neither knitting mouse nor mice in a shoe belong to the sequence shown here, but its first picture inspired the cover of *Appley Dapply's Nursery Rhymes*. Featuring variously as mother, waitress or nurse, the running mouse is less often included in letters or illustrations than the other two designs. Here she scurries off to the left, bringing broth in a tureen – but in a letter to Freda Moore (Winchelsea, 26 January 1900), Beatrix draws her landlady as a mouse with a steaming plate of food. In both these images the mouse runs to the left; but on the *Appley Dapply* cover the image is reversed. Now she is no longer the Old Woman mouse but Appley herself, running with a plate of jam tarts. Characteristically, Beatrix Potter is re-using her basic design, for a different rhyme.

E J SULLIVAN
Edmund Joseph Sullivan, RWS RE IS (1869-1933)

*'Sullivan was naturally the most gifted of the
younger black-and-white artists of my time,
not excepting Beardsley.'*

(A S Hartrick, *Painter's Pilgrimage Through Fifty Years*,
Cambridge University Press, 1939, page 156)

E J Sullivan was one of the most striking and confident
illustrators of his generation, ranging across many
moods and media, and becoming a particularly
influential teacher.

For a biography of Edmund Joseph Sullivan, please refer to
The Illustrators, 2016, pages 6-7.

The Man Who Influenced Arthur Rackham

Chris Beetles Gallery is pleased to announce an online
exhibition of the work of E J Sullivan, scheduled for year.
The greatest of gift book illustrators, Arthur Rackham,
acknowledged Sullivan as both a significant influence and
a close friend. He included him in his list of the '33 Greatest
Painters of the XIX Century' (held in the Rackham family
collections) and encouraged him to put himself up for election
to the Royal Society of Painters in Water-Colours.
Nevertheless, it was through his mastery of pen and ink
draughtsmanship that Sullivan most strongly affected Rackham.

5
THEN TO THE ROLLING HEAV'N ITSELF I CRIED
ASKING, 'WHAT LAMP HAD DESTINY TO GUIDE
HER LITTLE CHILDREN STUMBLING IN THE DARK?'
AND – 'A BLIND UNDERSTANDING!' HEAV'N REPLIED
Signed and dated 1912
Pen and ink on board
9 x 6 ¾ inches
Provenance: Brigadier A C Sykes of Corton, Wiltshire and by descent
Illustrated: Edward Fitzgerald, *The Rubaiyat of Omar Khayyam*, London: Methuen & Co, 1913, Verse XXXIII
Exhibited: Venice Biennale, 1914

6

THEN SAID ANOTHER WITH A
LONG-DRAWN SIGH,
'MY CLAY WITH LONG OBLIVION
IS GONE DRY:
BUT, FILL ME WITH THE OLD
FAMILIAR JUICE,
METHINKS I MIGHT RECOVER
BY-AND-BYE!'

Signed and dated 1907
Inscribed 'LXV' below mount
Pen and ink on board
7 ¾ x 5 ½ inches
Provenance: Brigadier A C Sykes of Corton,
Wiltshire and by descent
Illustrated: Edward Fitzgerald, *The Rubaiyat
of Omar Khayyam*, London:
Methuen & Co, 1913, Verse LXV

FRANK REYNOLDS
Frank Reynolds (1876-1953)

Drawing mainly from memory, Frank Reynolds became much admired for his direct characterisation of middle-class and low-life types and situations.

For a biography of Frank Reynolds, please refer to *The Illustrators*, 2011, page 130.

Frank Reynolds as a Book Illustrator

Frank Reynolds is best remembered as a cartoonist for *Punch*, and for his role as its art editor during the 1920s. However, he was on occasion an outstanding book illustrator, especially of novels by Charles Dickens, in editions published by Hodder: *David Copperfield* (1911), *The Pickwick Papers* (1912) and *The Old Curiosity Shop* (1913). In his illustrations, he applied watercolour with great sensitivity in order to capture the individual personality of each character. The specialist on illustration, A E Johnson, went so far as to state that 'until we see that wonderful gallery of fanciful personalities which began with Mr Pickwick and his companions portrayed by the pencil of Frank Reynolds, we shall have to wait still for the perfect edition of Dickens.' (*Frank Reynolds*, London: A & C Black, 1907, page 56).

7
AGNES
Signed and dated 1911
Watercolour with bodycolour and ink on board
14 ¼ x 8 ¼ inches
Illustrated: Charles Dickens, *The Personal History of David Copperfield*, London: Hodder & Stoughton, 1911, Facing Page 448

GEORG JANNY
Georg Janny (1864-1935)

Georg Janny was an Austrian theatre designer and easel painter, who developed an intriguingly atmospheric strain of fantasy painting, depicting rocky coasts inhabited by sirens and mountain gorges populated by fairies.

Georg Janny was born in Vienna on 20 May 1864, three years before it became one of the two capitals of the newly-established Austro-Hungarian Empire. He worked in the studios of Brioschi, Burghart and Kautsky, Imperial and Royal Court Theatre Painters in Vienna, alongside Alphonse Mucha, Konrad Petrides and Leopold Rothaug, among others. The company produced sets for companies abroad as well as at home, including New York's Metropolitan Opera. In 1898, Janny collaborated with Karl Schüller in painting the safety curtain at the Vienna Volksoper for the golden jubilee of Emperor Franz Joseph I.

Following the death of Hermann Burghart in 1901, Janny, Petrides and Rothaug took over the company, and based themselves at Paletzgasse 38. In 1904, they exhibited together at the Austrian Pavilion of the St Louis World's Fair with scenes from the Imperial Royal Austrian State Railways (that are now in the collections of the Technisches Museum, Vienna). Two years later, Janny produced the designs for a production at the Vienna State Opera of Karl Goldmark's *Die Königen von Saba*, one of the most popular operas of the late nineteenth century.

During the First World War, Janny turned from theatre design to easel painting. This was probably as an outcome of the impending dissolution of the Austro-Hungarian Empire, and the resulting lack of opportunities to work on elaborate theatrical productions. He painted landscapes and figures, including scenes from fairy tales or imaginary worlds, which were compared at the time to the works of Arnold Böcklin and Hermann Vogel. These he exhibited most regularly at the Kunstverein in Baden bei Wien and with the artists' co-operative, Albrecht-Dürer-Bundes, of which he was a member and sometime archivist. He died in Vienna on 21 February 1935.

The contents of his estate are now in the possession of the Hernals District Museum in Vienna.

(Detail of **8**)

8
STRANGER THINGS
Signed and dated 1920
Tempera with oil on board
18 ¾ x 13 ½ inches

9
ELFENSPIEL
[ELVISH GAMES]
Signed and dated 'Wien 1917'
Signed and inscribed with title
on reverse
Tempera on board
34 ¾ x 24 ¼ inches
Exhibited: 17th exhibition,
Albrecht Dürer-Bund, Vienna, 1918

THOMAS MACKENZIE
Thomas Blakeley Mackenzie (1888-1944)

Thomas Mackenzie was one of the last of the major illustrators of gift books, those beautifully produced editions of classic tales of wonder. He knowingly absorbed the influences of such major predecessors as Aubrey Beardsley, Kay Nielsen and Harry Clarke in order to create his own style. Skilled as a printmaker as well as a draughtsman and watercolourist, he made use of linocut and etching in responding to some of his later commissions.

Thomas Mackenzie was born in Bradford, Yorkshire, the elder son of the wool combing overlooker, James Bates Mackenzie, and his wife, Nellie (née Blakeley). At the time of his birth, the family was living at 3 Upper Pollard Street, Bowling. He was educated at a local board school, and then probably at Belle Vue Secondary School (Boys). It has been suggested that he began his close friendship with the future writer, J B Priestley (1894-1984), at Belle Vue. However, this is unlikely, given that Priestley arrived at the school in 1905, while Mackenzie finished his schooling in about 1903. By that time, he and his family had moved to 31 Balfour Street, and his father had established a wholesale business in bakery and confectionery.

Mackenzie was encouraged to develop his ability to draw by teachers at both his schools. However, his parents were apparently reluctant to let him pursue an artistic career. What happened next, and for the seven years of his life between the ages of 15 and 22, is not known. A story has circulated that he ran away to study in Munich, a significant artistic centre at the time. This has been accepted by Peter Cope (2011, page 9), but dismissed by Colin White (1988, page 11), who suggests instead that he undertook an apprenticeship (which conventionally took seven years), possibly as a draughtsman at a firm of engineers or printers.

At the time that Mackenzie entered Bradford School of Art in 1910, he and his family had moved to 443 Killinghall Road, and his father had become an insurance agent. While there, he met fellow student, Florence Mary Anderson, who, like him, would become an accomplished illustrator. In 1912, both he and she won scholarships for two years' study in drawing and painting at the Slade School of Art, in London, under Henry Tonks. However, Mackenzie left after a year, possibly because of an aesthetic disagreement or because he decided to seek paid work. In the meantime, he and Anderson had become lovers, and she gave birth to a son, Murray Anderson Mackenzie (in Epsom, Surrey, in May 1914). Murray would be brought up mostly by his grandparents in Yorkshire.

On leaving the Slade in 1913, Mackenzie went to the publisher and distributor, Simpkin, Marshall, Hamilton, Kent & Co, and presented his portfolio, which contained drawings that showed the influence of Aubrey Beardsley and Harry Clarke. As a result of the visit, he received a commission to illustrate a small volume of Christmas carols, and this would eventually be published in 1916 (with the illustrations being credited to 'T Mackenzie'). In the meantime, he made a somewhat uncertain living, mainly contributing drawings to *The Sketch* and other magazines. He also received an important commission from the publisher, James Nisbet, to illustrate *Aladdin and his Wonderful Lamp*, a large new gift book with a rhyming text by Arthur Ransome. However, this project was temporarily abandoned as a result of the increasing scale of the world war. In a letter of 15 February 1915, Ransome complained that Mackenzie had 'suddenly gone off to Serbia' on active service. ☞ *Page 18*

Scheherazade Dancing

Thomas Mackenzie was one of the most eclectic of gift book illustrators, who almost revelled in his absorption of influences. Here, in the figure of Scheherazade, he quotes most obviously from the work of Léon Bakst (1866-1924), the designer of sets and costumes most closely associated with Serge Diaghilev's Ballets Russes.

The Ballets Russes was one of the most culturally significant phenomena of the early twentieth century, employing and influencing many of the greatest figures working internationally in the fields of literature, music and the visual arts, as well as of dance itself. The company made its British debut in 1911, during the celebrations for the coronation of George V, and returned to London regularly both before and after the First World War, until 1922.

Mackenzie is likely to have attended performances of the Ballets Russes and undoubtedly saw reproductions of Bakst's costume designs. The company had created a ballet to the music of Rimsky-Korsakov's symphonic suite, *Scheherazade*, in 1910, but Mackenzie based his figure of Scheherazade on Bakst's design for the costume of a Boetian youth, a character in the ballet, *Narcisse*. *Narcisse* was choreographed by Michel Fokine to a specially-written score by Nikolai Tcherepnin, and premiered in Monte Carlo in April 1911, with Vaslav Nijinsky in the title role. *Narcisse* was the first of three Greek-themed ballets designed by Bakst, who had been making a thorough study of ancient Greek costume since 1902, when he prepared designs for productions of Greek tragedies in St Petersburg. He rejected the monochromaticism of Neo-Classicism in favour of a brighter palette and more exotic patterning, which was both more archaeologically accurate and visually exciting. The design for the Boetian youth was among those included in the book, *L'Art decoratif de Léon Bakst*, which was published in Paris in 1913.

10
SCHEHERAZADE DANCING
Signed
Pen ink, watercolour, bodycolour
and pencil on board
10 ¼ x 16 inches
Probably illustrated in *Ali Baba and Aladdin*,
London: George G Harrap, 1918

Biography of Thomas Mackenzie continued from Page 16

At the end of the First World War, Mackenzie bought Old Rushes, a cottage in the Hertfordshire village of Rushden, and this would remain his bolt hole for years to come. In 1918, Harrap published his first significant book, *Ali Baba and Aladdin*, his name appearing on it as 'T Blakeley Mackenzie'. In the following year, Nisbet finally published its version of *Aladdin* in both deluxe and trade editions in time for the Christmas market (the illustrator appearing simply as 'Mackenzie'). It was well received by the critics, and proved influential, even on the design by William Cameron Menzies of the 1924 film, *The Thief of Bagdad* (over which Mackenzie would consider legal action). Nisbet followed *Aladdin* with *Arthur and His Knights*, solely in a trade edition (1920), Mackenzie illustrating a text by his friend and Nisbet's juvenile book editor, Christine Chaundler. By 1921, he 'was said to be the best paid illustrator in the country' (White, 1988, page 27).

In the years immediately following the war, Mackenzie and Anderson 'rented various properties in and around London as well as travelling between London and Yorkshire singly or together', though 'they seem to have grown apart' (Cope, 2011, page 13). In 1921, while on a walking holiday in Yorkshire, he met Katharine Clayton, who had recently completed her studies in jewellery design at Birmingham School of Art. He and Clayton spent increasing amounts of time together, including a further visit to Yorkshire in 1923, during which he made preparatory drawings for the illustrations to his next book, for Bodley Head, which were executed in etching, linocut and watercolour. This was the non-fiction volume, *Brontë Moors and Villages from Thornton to Haworth*, by Elizabeth Southwart, whose work Anderson had also illustrated.

Mackenzie's next two illustrative projects were more characteristic, in being gift books that showcased his talents for, respectively, the Orientalist and the fantastic. These were James Elroy Flecker's play, *Hassan* (Heinemann, 1924), and James Stephens' *The Crock of Gold* (Macmillan, 1926), the latter appearing in both deluxe and trade editions.

Perhaps responding to a boom in etching, Mackenzie worked increasingly as a printmaker, and exhibited etchings and engravings with the London dealer, Alex Reid & Lefèvre. It is therefore understandable that his last two books should be illustrated with forms of print, linocuts for F J Harvey Darton's *A Parcel of Kent* (Nisbet, 1926), and drypoints for a two-volume limited edition of Walter Pater's *Marius the Epicurean* (Macmillan, 1929, with an introduction by Mackenzie's friend, the poet and critic, J C Squire).

In 1925, Mackenzie and Anderson had married at Hampstead Registry Office in order to make Murray legitimate. However, shortly afterwards, Anderson filed for divorce on the grounds of Mackenzie's adultery. Cope explains that 'It is on record that the presiding judge suspected collusion between the parties, but subsequent enquiries failed to substantiate his view' (2011, page 14). The divorce was granted in October 1928.

In January 1929, Mackenzie married Katharine Clayton at Hampstead Registry Office. Soon after, they left for Paris, where Mackenzie hoped to fulfil a long-held dream of establishing himself as a painter. Inspired by the formal qualities of both Piero della Francesca and Cézanne, he had for some time been producing landscapes and still lifes. However, he did not succeed in his plan, and after six months they returned to live at his cottage in Rushden with their savings depleted. He then survived by contributing to magazines and selling topographical etchings to gift shops (including views of Oxford), while Katharine produced jewellery. In 1936, he exhibited at the Royal Academy for his one and only time; the work, entitled *Tuning Up*, was probably an etching.

In 1937, the Mackenzies moved to Cornwall, and settled in a stone cottage in Trewetha Lane, Trewetha, near Port Isaac. There they founded a summer school for paying students, which initially proved a success, but was forced to close following the outbreak of the Second World War. In the Register for 1939, Mackenzie described himself as 'artist, designer, etcher, lithographer, visualiser', and Katharine as 'artist, jeweller, etcher'. They returned to making jewellery and, in his spare time, Mackenzie wrote detective novels; however, he thought none of them worthy of publication and requested that, following his death, they be destroyed.

Thomas Mackenzie died of lung cancer at home in Trewetha on 8 December 1944, at the age of 56. His ashes were scattered over Buckden Moor, Yorkshire, where he and Katharine had first met.

Further reading

Peter Cope, 'Heart v Art: Florence Mary Anderson and Thomas Mackenzie', *Illustration*, Spring 2011, pages 8-15;
Colin White, 'Thomas Mackenzie and the Beardsley legacy', *Journal of Decorative and Propaganda Arts*, Winter 1988, pages 6-35

FRANK BRANGWYN
Sir Frank William Brangwyn, RA HRSA RSW RWS PRBA RE HRMS ROI (1867-1956)

Frank Brangwyn fulfilled his own belief, stated in 1934, that an artist 'must be able to turn his hand to everything, for his mission is to decorate life'. Though modest about his own achievements, he was ambitious in the range and scale of his art, creating large-scale murals, oils and watercolours, illustrations and prints, ceramics, furniture, stained-glass and textiles, in emulation of traditional workshop practice. He was particularly successful at arranging large numbers of figures into complex compositions that vary in mood from impassioned to celebratory.

For a biography of Frank Brangwyn, please refer to *The Illustrators*, 1999, pages 128-129.

11
TRIA JUNCTA IN UNO
BOOKPLATE FOR W RUHR
Signed
Inscribed 'Morland Press' on reverse
Ink and chalk
18 x 17 inches
Provenance: William de Belleroche;
Vivien Noakes
Illustrated: Eden Phillpotts (foreword),
Bookplates by Frank Brangwyn, London:
The Morland Press, 1920, Plate 68

CHARLES REBEL STANTON
Charles Rebel Stanton (1887-1954)

At its most characteristic, the art of Charles Rebel Stanton exemplifies the Jazz Age in Britain, encompassing as it does both images of flappers for popular illustrated magazines and an Art Deco relief for the Queen Mary. Said to be trained as an architect, he became successful as an illustrator, painter and sculptor, and produced a range of work that included powerful scenes of devastation in both world wars.

Charles Rebel Stanton was born in Kentish Town, London, on 3 February 1887, the third of seven children of the book seller's assistant, Charles Stanton, and his wife, Amelia (née Tate). At the time of the 1891 Census, the family was living at 22 Corinne Road, Islington. Nothing is known of Stanton's education but, at the time of the 1901 Census, when he was 14 years old, he was working as a Science Assistant for the School Board of London, probably at a local school. By then, he and his family had moved to 121 South Street, Greenwich, and his father was working as a carpenter.

In *The Art of the RMS Queen Mary* (1994), Douglas M Hinkey describes Stanton as 'a painter trained as an architect'. While nothing is known of his architectural training, he is described as an 'artist' in the 1911 Census, which also records that he was still living with his family, which had moved to 53 Grosvenor Park SE, St Mary Newington. In the previous year, he had won second prize in the class for 'pictorial art' in a competition organised by the magazine, *The Studio*.

Charles Stanton began his career as a commercial artist, designing posters and postcards and illustrating books, and signing his work 'Charles R Stanton'. Commissions included a poster for the Fine Art Society that was general enough in its design to have been used to advertise any number of exhibitions (though the example that has come to light promoted 'Water Colours of Flower Time … by Rosa Wallis' of 1911). His postcard designs ranged between imaginary monsters (published by C W Faulkner & Co) and views of Minehead and Dunster (published by Frith). He also contributed illustrations to *Hutchinson's History of the Nations* (1914-16).

Following the outbreak of the First World War in 1914, Stanton enlisted as a Private in the First Surrey Rifles in March 1915. He became a Second Lieutenant in September of that year and a Lieutenant in the following June. One of his younger brothers, John Tate Stanton, served in the same regiment, and died in 1916. Though not an official war artist during the First World War, Stanton produced a number of watercolours of the devastated landscapes of Belgium and northern France while on active service. He also designed a Christmas card for the regiment.

Charles Rebel Stanton sketching the design for the nickel-coated panel on the RMS Queen Mary

It has been suggested that Stanton began to make use of his middle name, Rebel, during the First World War. Certainly, he signed his work 'C Rebel Stanton' after the war, and was sometimes known simply as Rebel Stanton. From the early 1920s, he designed book covers for publishers that included Mills & Boon. Gradually, he established his reputation with watercolours of alluring young women that were published in such magazines as *The Bystander*, *The Illustrated London News*, *Picture Post*, *The Sketch* and *The Tatler*. He also worked as a painter in oils, producing not only landscapes but also a series symbolising the progress of transport through the ages, which was commissioned for Transport House, the London headquarters of the Transport and General Workers' Union. In 1926, he married Eunice Emily Cantrell Stones, who was 12 years his junior, and they settled together at a flat in Warren House, 295 Euston Road. In 1930, he would hold an exhibition at his studio in Warren House.

During the early 1930s, Stanton spent two years perfecting a new form of relief, in which he superimposed layers of American whitewood, which he then painted in tempera or oil. The process was described in H B Newbold's *Modern Practical Building* (which first appeared in 1934). Examples of these reliefs included medallions of Derby winners that temporarily decorated the Plaza Hall, Dublin, the venue of the Irish Sweepstake draw (1932) and a frieze for an aerodrome administration block, commissioned by the Fairby Construction Company (1935). Most famous, however, was the nickel-coated mural panel that incorporated a clock, which he produced for the Second Class Lounge of the Queen Mary (1935). This was a particularly prestigious commission, as the liner was something of a floating ambassador and showcased the talents of many of Britain's leading artists. Stanton also developed a line in decorative masks, including one of the comic actor,

Will Hay, which graced the bohemian Arts and Letters Club, in Ham Yard, Soho, of which the artist was a member (1937).

By 1936, Stanton had divorced his wife Eunice (who, in that year, would marry a pottery agent called Gordon Munro). He was living at 101 Adelaide Road, Chalk Farm, in 1937, and at 24 Formosa Street, Maida Vale, two years later.

During the Second World War, Stanton produced drawings and paintings of bomb damaged buildings in London, and specifically of the Holborn area between September 1940 and July 1941. However, it is uncertain whether he ever received a commission from the War Artists' Advisory Committee to produce such images. (In a PhD thesis of 1991, B F Foss records that he made four unsuccessful applications to the WAAC.)

By 1946, Stanton was based at Redcliffe Road, in Kensington. In that year, he produced The Silver Star Statuette, the hallmarked silver trophy for the new National Film Award, based on a competition-winning design by a young Southport schoolteacher, Juliet Brothers. Three such statuettes were presented annually by the *Daily Mail* for the best British film, and the best performance by an actor and an actress in British films.

His work is represented in the collections of the Cuming Museum, Art Collection and Local History Library and Archive (Southwark).

12
GHOULIES AND GHOOSTIES
Signed
Watercolour and bodycolour
23 x 17 ¾ inches
Illustrated: *The Sketch*, 6 April 1927,
Page 18

HELEN JACOBS
Helen Mary Jacobs, BWS (1888-1970)

Talented in both draughtsmanship and watercolour painting, Helen Jacobs soon established herself as a children's illustrator. Though best known for the precision, energy and imagination of her early fairy subjects, she responded well to a variety of commissions; and, as a primary teacher, she seemed an ideal interpreter of textbooks and primers.

Helen Jacobs was born in Ilford, Essex, on 10 October 1888, the daughter of the wharf manager, William Jacobs, and his second wife, Ellen (née Flory). The youngest member of the family, she had four half-siblings, the eldest of whom was the popular writer, W W Jacobs, and four siblings. She spent her childhood in Stoke Newington, London, at addresses that included 112 Manor Road (by 1891) and 3 Paradise Row (by 1901).

Jacobs studied under Arthur Legge at the art school of the West Ham Municipal College. While there, in 1910, she contributed a box, painted with characteristic fairies, to the National Competitions of Schools of Art, which was illustrated in The Studio. From that year, she began to exhibit watercolours at mixed exhibitions, including those organised by the Royal Academy of Arts, the Royal Institute of Painters in Water-Colours and the Dudley Gallery. It may be assumed that, as a member of the British Watercolour Society, she was also represented in its exhibitions. In addition, she produced a series of drawings of species of moth for the entomologist, Lord Rothschild.

Jacobs quickly established herself as a children's illustrator, working mainly in watercolour and pen and ink. She contributed to annuals (including Pip & Squeak and Playbox) and periodicals (including The Sunday Fairy), while responding increasingly to commissions from major publishers, most notably Harrap.

While beginning to establish herself, in the years 1911-12, Jacobs had lived with her sister, Florence, at Carisbrooke, Osborne Road, Buckhurst Hill, Essex. However, by 1914, she had returned to London and settled in Winchmore Hill, living at 34 Queen's Avenue by 1917, and remaining there until her death.

In her later years, Jacobs taught at a primary school in Stoke Newington, and turned to illustrating school books and primers. These included frequent collaborations with her friend Stella Mead ('The Open Road' series, and other Nisbet publications, and later titles published by the University of London Press) and some with Constance M Martin (particularly the 'Riverside Readers', published by Philip & Tacey). The pedagogic material led to a move away from the precise beauty of her early fairy watercolours to a brighter, bolder graphic style.

Helen Jacobs died on 15 December 1970.

13
FAIRY PAINTERS
Signed
Watercolour, pen ink and bodycolour
14 ½ x 10 ¼ inches
Provenance: Bierrum Family
Illustrated: The Bookman, Special Christmas Number, 1933;
J H Steel, An Introduction to the King's English B, London: James Nisbet & Co, 1945, Page 64

Nos **15** & **16** were drawn for and probably Illustrated in Constance M Martin, *The Wild Swans and Other Stories*, ('the Golden Readers' Series

15 (left)
THE FAIRY
GODMOTHER
Pen and ink
7 x 4 ½ inches

16
THE GOBLIN HID
BEHIND THE BARREL
Pen and ink with pencil
7 x 5 inches
Illustrated: 'The Goblin and the Grocer'

14
THE ELVES AND FAIRIES CAME TO GREET THEM,
BEARING THEIR QUAINT OFFERINGS
Signed
Pen and ink, 10 ¾ x 7 ½ inches
Provenance: The Estate of Constance M Martin
Illustrated: C M Martin (Reteller and Editor), *Legends From the Norse* (the 'Riverside' Series No 10), London: Martins Press, [1948], Page 24, 'Frey and Gerda'
Exhibited: 'The Turn of Women Artists 1837-2018', Chris Beetles Gallery,March-April 2018, No 112

IDA RENTOUL OUTHWAITE
Ida Sherbourne Rentoul Outhwaite (1888-1960)

The originality of Ida Rentoul Outhwaite lies in the way that she grafted elements of the Australian outback onto the English fairy tradition and so created a mythology that is at once national and personal.

Ida Rentoul Outhwaite was born Ida Rentoul in Carlton, Melbourne, Victoria, Australia, on 9 June 1888, the younger of the two surviving children of the Reverend John Lawrence Rentoul, a Presbyterian minister and professor of theology at Ormond College, University of Melbourne, and his wife, Annie (née Rattray). She was educated at the Presbyterian Ladies' College, Melbourne, where she proved herself to be academically brilliant.

In 1903, at the age of 15, Ida began to work closely with her writer sister, Annie, and in that year they contributed six illustrated fairy stories to the weekly magazine, *The New Idea: A Woman's Home Journal for Australasia*. They refined their collaboration in the following year in their first book, *Mollie and the Bunyip*, which was well received. The collaboration was then developed in the first of their famous songbooks, *Australian Songs for Young and Old*, with music by Georgette Peterson, which was launched at the Australian Exhibition of Women's Work, Melbourne, in October 1907. In the December of the same year, the sisters produced a pantomime book, *The Story of the Pantomime Humpty Dumpty*, to accompany a production at Her Majesty's Theatre, Melbourne, for which Ida had designed the costumes. Printed in chromolithographic colour, its illustrations – inspired by the work of Walter Crane – indicated a greater versatility and a particular feel for comedy. The many strands of Ida's early work were brought together in 1908 in both the first Australian edition of her sister's version of *Peter Pan* and their first substantial story book, *The Lady of the Blue Beads*.

In 1909, Ida married Arthur Grenbry Outhwaite, manager – and later managing director – of the Perpetual Executors and Trustees Association of Australia. Together they had four children, all of whom served as models for the figures in her later illustrations. The second phase of her career was launched by an exhibition at the Fine Art Society, Melbourne, in September 1916. This coincided with the publication of *Elves and Fairies*, which made much of the ability of new printing

17
THE GUESTS WENT INTO CONFERENCE
Signed with initials
Inscribed with title below mount
Watercolour
10 ¼ x 8 inches

processes to reproduce the subtleties of watercolour. Further shows followed and, on her first trip to England in 1920, Outhwaite exhibited at the Fine Art Society, London. Her success led to a series of five colour-plate books by A & C Black. These included *The Enchanted Forest* (1921), the first of her collaborations with her husband, and *The Little Green Road to Fairyland* (1922), probably her most popular collaboration with her sister. In her later books, fairies were displaced from their central position by animals, a change that reflected wider shifts in fashion. Unfortunately, this did not prove popular with her readership.

Ida's husband, Arthur Outhwaite, died in 1938, and both their sons died in action in the Second World War, during which she worked in censorship. She spent her last years with her unmarried sister living in a flat in Caulfield, a suburb of Melbourne.

She died in Caulfield on 25 June 1960.

Further reading
Diane Langmore, 'Outhwaite, Ida Sherbourne (1888–1960)', *Australian Dictionary of Biography*, National Centre of Biography, Australian National University, http://adb.anu.edu.au/biography/outhwaite-ida-sherbourne-7933/text13807, published first in hardcopy 1988;
Marcie Muir and Robert Holden, *The Fairy World of Ida Rentoul Outhwaite*, Sydney: Craftsman House, 1985

18
THE ECHIDNA PERFORMED
Signed with initials
Inscribed with title below mount
Watercolour
10 ¼ x 8 inches

2 Early
20th Century
Cartoon &
Caricature

PHIL MAY
Philip William May, RI RP NEAC
(1864-1903)

Sometimes referred to as the 'grandfather of British illustration',
Phil May was one of the most influential black-and-white artists of
his generation. Earthy, street-wise, and redolent of the music hall,
his work is the antithesis of Aubrey Beardsley.

For a biography of Phil May, please refer to *The Illustrators*, 2017, page 36.

19
GUTTERSNIPES
DESIGN FOR THE LETTER A
Signed
Pen and ink, 4 ½ x 3 inches
Similar to *Phil May's ABC: Fifty-Two Original Designs Forming Two Humorous
Alphabets From A to Z*, London: Leadenhall Press, 1897

" What's that there blank space left for Jim ? "
" Why, that's for the folks as can't read ! "

20 (opposite)
'WHAT'S THAT THERE BLANK
SPACE LEFT FOR JIM?'
'WHY THAT'S FOR THE FOLKS
AS CAN'T READ!'
Signed and dated 1900
Preliminary sketch on reverse
Pen and ink
10 ½ x 7 inches
Provenance: Luke Gertler Collection
Illustrated: *Punch*, 28 March 1900, Page 217

21
THE GUTTERSNIPES
'PLEASE, SIR, TUPPENCE WORTH OF BUTTER
SCRAPINGS AN' MOTHER SAYS BE SURE THEY'RE
ALL CLEAN 'CAUSE SHE'S EXPECTING COMPANY'
Signed and dated /99
Inscribed with title below mount
Pen and ink
8 ½ x 6 inches
Illustrated: *Punch*, 3 May 1899, Page 207;
David Cuppleditch, *Phil May, the Artist and His Wit*,
London: The Fortune Press, 1981, Page 115
Exhibited: 'The Fine Art of Illustration', The Fine
Art Society, London, July 2001

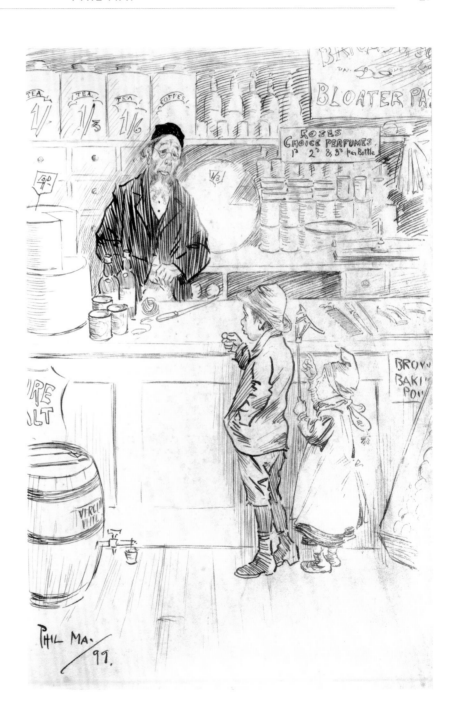

MAX BEERBOHM

Sir Henry Maximillian Beerbohm, IS NEAC NPS (1872-1956)

Equally valued as a caricaturist and writer, Max Beerbohm sustained an elegant detachment in art and life. Though the tone of his drawings is often lightly wicked, it is also affectionate, for he hated to wound his subjects, most of whom he knew and liked. As a result, he was on safest ground in satirising artists and writers of the past, and in making many self-caricatures.

For a biography of Max Beerbohm, please refer to *The Illustrators*, 2014, page 89.

'the greatest caricaturist of the kind – that is, portrayer of personalities – in the history of art'

(Edmund Wilson, 1954, quoted in S N Behrman, *Portrait of Max: an intimate memoir of Sir Max Beerbohm*, New York: Random House, 1960, page 262)

King Edward the Seventh

'Both as Prince of Wales and as King, Edward VII (1841-1910) was Max's favourite subject. The Hart-Davis Catalogue lists 72 caricatures of him (a number only surpassed by self-caricatures …). The Prince and later King was vulgar: he had next to no book learning; he cared little for the arts beyond theatre-going; his delights were the race course, the gambling table, food and drink, and, notoriously, philandering …

Max, while still a schoolboy, began caricaturing the Prince of Wales, and never left off. There are those who feel Max despised Edward, but their view fails to take into account Max's sense of fun, his love of irony, his genuine delight in anything touching the ridiculous, his broad sympathy for simple souls, whatever their position in life …

As King, Edward fascinated Max more than ever. He drew him constantly and unsparingly. One of Edward's "salient" features was his large, pointed nose. Max said, à propos of the King, "The noses of fat men do not follow suit with the rest of them as they age. The noses become, if anything, sharper, thinner"'.

(N John Hall, *Max Beerbohm. Caricatures*, New Haven: Yale University Press,1997, pages 171-173)

Left: *Max Beerbohm, possibly while living at Abinger Manor Cottage, Surrey,during the Second World War*
(for more information, please see the note to **24**)

22
KING EDWARD
THE SEVENTH
Signed and inscribedwith title
Pen ink and watercolour
8 ½ x 7 ¾ inches

A Nightmare

The American writer, Henry James (1843-1916), settled in England in 1876, and wrote most of his major works from that time. He became the favourite novelist of Max Beerbohm and, when Beerbohm first met him in 1895, he found the man as fascinating as his books. Between 1898 and 1954, Beerbohm produced at least 22 affectionate caricatures of James that cleverly critique his authorial personality and literary style.

James gained a reputation for producing psychologically acute narratives that examined inevitable and universal conflicts of moral character. He became increasingly experimental in his attempts to represent complex states of mind and ambiguous motives, forming long paragraphs that proceed indirectly by way of suggestive, shifting rumination. This approach was affected, from 1897, by his change of practice, from writing his own drafts to dictating to a typist.

The most significant results of James's experimentation were three late novels: *The Wings of a Dove* (1902), *The Ambassadors* (1903) and *The Golden Bowl* (1904). These were particularly loved by Beerbohm, though he was aware that their stylistic idiosyncrasies were replete with difficulty and ripe for parody. As both writer and artist, he was able to respond in word as well as image; so he provided captions to his caricatures that succinctly mimic James's mode of expression, and also penned a more substantial pastiche, 'The Mote in the Middle Distance', which first appeared in the *Saturday Review* on 8 December 1906, as part of his second 'Christmas Garland'.

The present caricature was exhibited two years later, in April 1908, in an exhibition at Carfax & Co, London. It portrays James as an expert witness in a court of law, in the deliciously impossible position of being asked to provide a 'plain answer' to a 'plain question'. It is unlikely to relate to a specific 'cause célèbre', though the figures seated behind the author look as if they may have stepped out of one of James's novels. In his catalogue of Beerbohm's caricatures, Rupert Hart-Davis notes that both James's solicitor, Sir George Lewis, and Lewis's son are among those present, being seated below left of the 'Cross-Examining Counsel'. The study for this caricature was entitled 'An Awful Fancy …' rather than 'A Nightmare …'. The final choice of words leaves the spectator wondering whether the 'nightmare' is that of Henry James or of one of his less sympathetic readers.

23

A NIGHTMARE. MR HENRY JAMES SUBPOENA'D, AS PSYCHOLOGICAL EXPERT, IN A CAUSE CÉLÈBRE

CROSS-EXAMINING COUNSEL: 'COME SIR, I ASK YOU A PLAIN QUESTION, AND I EXPECT A PLAIN ANSWER!'

Signed and dated 1908
Inscribed with title on original mount
Watercolour and pencil
11 ¼ x 16 inches
Provenance: Miss Elizabeth Williamson
Literature: Rupert Hart-Davis, *A Catalogue of the Caricatures of Max Beerbohm*, London: Macmillan, 1972, No 805.
(Rupert Hart-Davis notes in his entry that 'the only other recognisable people in court are Sir George Lewis and his son'.)
Exhibited: 'Caricatures by Max Beerbohm', Carfax & Co, London, April-May 1908

Cashmere – and again the queue!

In the summer of 1908, the American artist, John Singer Sargent (1856-1925), exhibited his oil painting, *Cashmere*, at the Royal Academy (as No 496). It depicted his niece, Reine Ormond, wearing a large exotic patterned shawl and standing in seven different positions against a verdant background. The effect is of seven similar women walking together, and is perhaps suggestive of both the Aesthetic paintings of Albert Moore and the Classical friezes that inspired them, though with an Orientalist twist. It also relates to a number of other works that Sargent produced of women in shawls (as Leigh Culver has explored in the fascinating dissertation, 'Performing Identities in the Art of John Singer Sargent', University of Pennsylvania, 1999).

At the time of its exhibition, Sargent's *Cashmere* was the subject of much comment, which attempted both to define and deny a possible meaning. Contributions to this comment were not only written but also drawn, as is epitomised by the present work by Max Beerbohm, who caricatured Sargent some 22 times. Exhibited at the New English Art Club in 1909, a year after *Cashmere* appeared at the RA, it replicates the composition of the painting and adds the figures of Sargent and an interpreter employed by the travel agent, Thomas Cook. In so doing, it locates the setting to the English protectorate of Kashmir, the northernmost region of the Indian subcontinent, a place that Sargent never actually visited. The young women comprise a queue of natives keen that Sargent paint their portraits. They may not be aware that Sargent had tired of accepting portrait commissions and, in 1907, had officially closed his studio. From that time, he focussed increasingly on landscapes and architectural subjects, including many in watercolour, and also completed the series of murals for public buildings in Massachusetts.

24

CASHMERE – AND AGAIN THE QUEUE!

MR SARGENT (TO COOK'S INTERPRETER): 'WHAT IS IT THEY WANT? WHAT? ... NO! CONFOUND IT: REALLY, THIS IS TOO BAD! DON'T THEY KNOW I'VE MADE UP MY MIND, ABSOLUTELY AND IRREVOCABLY, NOT TO ACCEPT ANY MORE COMMISSIONS?'

Signed, inscribed with title and dated 1909
Pen ink, watercolour and pencil
12 ¼ x 16 inches
Provenance: Miss Elizabeth Williamson
Illustrated: Max Beerbohm, *Fifty Caricatures*, New York: E P Dutton & Company, 1913
Literature: Rupert Hart-Davis, *A Catalogue of the Caricatures of Max Beerbohm*, London: Macmillan, 1972, No 1368
Exhibited: New English Art Club, Summer 1909, No 203

Cashmere — and again the queue!

Mr. Sargent (to Cook's interpreter): "What is it they want? What?... No! confound it! really, this is too bad! Don't they know that I've made up my mind, absolutely and irrevocably, not to accept any more commissions?

max 1909

Max Beerbohm and Maurice Baring

Only two years his elder, Max Beerbohm became a close friend of the writer, Maurice Baring (1874-1945), a member of the famous banking family. They probably met in 1893, at one of the Sunday evening suppers held at the London home of Edmund Gosse (now best remembered for his memoir, *Father and Son*). Beerbohm was then establishing himself as a dandy and humourist, while Baring was studying towards the examination for the Diplomatic Service. Both charming and amusing, they amused and charmed each other.

Baring's career in diplomacy proved abortive. Having developed a love of Russia, on trips made in 1900 and 1902, and having begun to learn Russian, he decided, late in 1904, to return to the country, master the language, and use his knowledge and experience as catalysts for a literary career. As a result, he produced eye-witness reports on the Russo-Japanese War for the *London Morning Post*, and, in June 1905, published his account, *With the Russians in Manchuria. Russian Essays and Stories* followed in 1908. In the April of that year, Beerbohm held an exhibition of caricatures at Carfax & Co, which included *Mr Maurice Baring, Testing Carefully the Russian Sense of Humour* [26, see overleaf], one of several that he made of his friend. Beerbohm 'claimed to treasure all [Baring's] books, with the exception of those about Russia, which he … admitted might have been his own blind spot' (Joseph Epstein, 'Maurice Baring & the good high-brow', *The New Criterion*, October 1992, page 18). The emphasis of the present caricature is therefore less the character of Baring *per se* than the incongruity of this gently humorous man engaging with the ceaselessly brooding, soul-searching Russians.

Nevertheless, Baring certainly absorbed the influence of contemporary Russian literature into his own writing, and was prescient in doing so, as is evidenced by his play, *The Grey Stocking*, which appeared at the New Royalty Theatre, London, in 1908. It reveals the impact of Anton Chekhov's *Uncle Vanya* six years before its British premiere, and three years before the British premiere of any of Chekhov's plays. Beerbohm's report of Baring's play, published in the *Saturday Review*, was, like that of other critics, perhaps inevitably lukewarm, and concluded that Baring was essentially an 'a dramatist' who dealt merely 'in humdrum and you and me'.

Baring proved more immediately successful as the author of such urbane and witty short stories as those collected in *Diminutive Dramas* (1910); these included 'The Member for Literature', which featured Beerbohm himself as one of four living writers standing for a parliamentary constituency, and provided him with a long speech that parodied his characteristic style. Beerbohm would repay the compliment by parodying Baring in 'All Roads', a piece that delighted the victim when he read it, though it was published only in 1950, five years after Baring's death, in a final edition of *A Christmas Garland*.

In reviewing *Diminutive Dramas*, as part of a wider profile of Baring in *The Bookman* in February 1913, Robert Birkmyre compared the comic approaches of Baring and Beerbohm:

> Although 'Max' catches to the life the speech and gesture of the subjects whom he parodies he does not give us the fine exuberant flavour, and the boisterous mirth that we find in the best examples of Mr Baring's treatment of the parody … [However,] we would not for the world under-estimate the inimitable 'Max' even in favour of so agreeable author as Mr Maurice Baring.

One of Baring's strengths was his ability to employ different genres in the reframing of his qualities of exuberance and mirth. So, in 1910, he also published a collection of fairy tales, *The Glass Mender and Other Stories*. It is this to which Beerbohm alludes in *Mr Maurice Baring, Telling a Fairy Story* [25], in which Baring entertains a throng of 'Beauties', 'that succession of lovely women with whom Maurice populated his life' (Emma Letley, *Maurice Baring: A Citizen of Europe*, London: Constable, page 196), even though he probably remained celibate.

In his lifetime, Baring was considered a major writer, and there have been sterling attempts to revive interest in his life and work, including that by Paul Horgan. In reviewing Paul Horgan's collection, *Maurice Baring Restored* (1970), the great American literary critic, Edmund Wilson, recommended 'four departments' of Baring's work worth rediscovering: 'his eight books about Russia … his long novel called simply *C* [1924] … the sequence of burlesques and parodies that he published between 1910 and 1913 … [and] his literary criticism, with which must be considered his anthologies' ('How Not to be Bored by Maurice Baring', *The Devils and Canon Barham*, New York: Farrar, Strauss and Giroux, 1973). However, he also admitted that the quintessence of Baring might lie in Beerbohm's parodies of him, and it may be through them that his presence ultimately survives.

25
MR MAURICE BARING, TELLING A FAIRY STORY
Signed and dated 1911
Inscribed with title on original mount
Watercolour and pencil with pen and ink
16 x 12 ¼ inches
Provenance: Miss Elizabeth Williamson
Literature: Rupert Hart-Davis, *A Catalogue of the Caricatures of Max Beerbohm*, London: Macmillan, 1972, No 89
Exhibited: London Group, 1911

26 (above)
MR MAURICE BARING, TESTING CAREFULLY THE
RUSSIAN SENSE OF HUMOUR
Signed, inscribed with title and dated 1908
Watercolour and pencil, 14 x 16 inches
Provenance: Miss Elizabeth Williamson
Literature: Rupert Hart-Davis, *A Catalogue of the Caricatures
of Max Beerbohm*, London: Macmillan, 1972, No 88
Exhibited: 'Caricatures by Max Beerbohm', Carfax & Co,
London, April-May 1908

27 (opposite)
SCHOLAR POET R C T
[R C TREVELYAN, 1872-1951]
Signed, inscribed with title and dated 1941
Pencil with watercolour
10 ¼ x 5 ½ inches
Illustrated: *The Abinger Chronicle*, Vol 2, No 7, October 1941;
R C Trevelyan, *Selected Poems*, London: MacGibbon & Kee, 1953
Literature: Rupert Hart-Davis, *A Catalogue of the Caricatures
of Max Beerbohm*, London: Macmillan, 1972, No 1681

Scholar Poet R C T

During the Second World War, Max Beerbohm developed a friendship with the poet and translator, Robert Calverley Trevelyan (1872-1951). Like his younger brother, the historian, G M Trevelyan, R C Trevelyan had been a member of the elite intellectual society, the Apostles, while at Cambridge. Consequently, he became a friend of members of the Bloomsbury Group, including E M Forster, with whom he travelled to India in 1912. Trevelyan had married the Dutch violinist, Elizabeth van der Hoeven, in 1900, and they settled at The Shiffolds, in Surrey, about four miles from Dorking. There they brought up their son, the artist, Julian Trevelyan, who was born in 1910. Robert's translations – mainly from Greek and Latin, and including three plays by Sophocles – influenced his own poetry and verse dramas.

On the eve of war, in January 1939, Beerbohm and his wife, Florence, left their home in Rapallo, on the Italian Riviera, and returned to England. They moved into Abinger Manor Cottage, a small Tudor house owned by their friends, the writer, translator and patron, Sydney Schiff, and his wife, Violet. It was located in the village of Abinger Common a mile or so north of The Shiffolds, the home of the Trevelyans.

The parish of Abinger had attracted creative figures for some years, including E M Forster, who, since 1925, had lived at his family home at Abinger Hammer. In 1939, a number of these figures came together to found the monthly literary magazine, *The Abinger Chronicle*, published by R C Trevelyan and edited by Sylvia Sprigge. the wife of the *Manchester Guardian* journalist, Cecil Sprigge. Apart from Beerbohm, Forster and Trevelyan, the chief contributors to *The Abinger Chronicle* were Oliver Lodge, Desmond McCarthy and the composer, Ralph Vaughan Williams (a contemporary of Beerbohm's at Charterhouse).

Beerbohm drew the present affectionate caricature of Trevelyan for the October 1941 issue of *The Abinger Chronicle*. In her memorial essay, 'Max in Abinger', published in *The Twentieth Century* in July 1956, Sylvia Sprigge described Trevelyan as 'a heavily-booted, tall, striding scholar-poet, with a tiny rucksack on his kindly, stooping back containing one or two books to read' (page 66); this exactly matches the image presented by Beerbohm.

Early on the morning of 3 August 1944, the Beerbohms' Abinger home was almost demolished by debris, as a result of the bombing of the nearby church. They survived, though their landlord, Sydney Schiff, died two months later, possibly as a result of the shock. They eventually found refuge with Ralph and Violet Wood at Flint Cottage, Box Hill, north of Dorking (which was once the home of the Victorian novelist, George Meredith). Their move may have contributed to the folding of *The Abinger Chronicle*, the last issue of which appeared in September 1944.

Evenings in Printing House Square

Alfred Harmsworth, 1st Viscount Northcliffe (1865-1922), was a powerful publishing magnate, who resuscitated unprofitable newspapers by making them popular to a mass market. He developed Amalgamated Press, the largest publishing empire in the world at the time, which included, among others: the *Evening News* (acquired 1894), the *Daily Mail* (founded 1896), the *Daily Mirror* (founded 1903), the *Observer* (acquired 1905), *The Times* and *The Sunday Times* (both acquired 1908). The present caricature refers to that latest acquisition.

Harmsworth had a good working relationship with Max Beerbohm, providing articles and caricatures for his publications. In December 1896, Beerbohm had taken up the invitation of Harmsworth to write a regular column for the newly-founded *Daily Mail*, on any subject that he wished. The results had, what one biographer of Beerbohm has called, 'the kind of smart-alecky hook that Harmsworth liked' (N John Hall, *Max Beerbohm: A Kind of Life*, London: Yale University Press, 2002, pages 50-51).

Following Harmsworth's acquisition of the magazine, *Vanity Fair*, eight years later, in 1904, Beerbohm contributed eight caricatures. Appearing between 1905 and 1909, they were initially signed with the pseudonyms, Ruth and Bilbo, Harmsworth thinking 'it would be commercially better that people should wonder who the cartoonist was who drew so like [Beerbohm]' (quoted in N John Hall, 1997, page 98). However, while admiring them, he 'hesitated to publish them … because he thought them libellous' (N John Hall, 2002, page 232).

In Autumn 1906, Harmsworth discovered that Beerbohm had never been to Italy, so suggested that he visit the country and write a series of travel articles for that newspaper. The trip changed the course of his life, as he became determined to live in Italy and, in 1910, did so, settling at Rapallo with his new wife, Florence.

28
EVENINGS IN PRINTING HOUSE SQUARE
LORD NORTHCLIFFE: 'HELP! AGAIN I FEEL THE DEMONS OF SENSATIONALISM RISING IN ME. HOLD ME FAST! CURB ME, IF YOU LOVE ME!'
Signed, inscribed with title and dated 1911
Pen ink and watercolour with pencil
12 ¼ x 15 ½ inches
Provenance: *The Times*;
The Jeffrey Archer Political Cartoon Collection
Illustrated: Max Beerbohm, *Fifty Caricatures*, London: William Heinemann, 1913, No 38
Literature: Rupert Hart-Davis, *A Catalogue of the Caricatures of Max Beerbohm*, London: Macmillan, 1972, No 1118

Exhibited: NEAC, Winter 1911;
London Group, 1913;
'Pure Gold. 50 Years of the Federation of British Artists', Mall Galleries, February 2011;
'The Long Nineteenth Century: Treasures and Pleasures', Chris Beetles Gallery, March-April 2014, No 143

Cold-Shouldered Yet

In December 1911, Andrew Bonar Law became Leader of the Conservative Party, following the resignation of Arthur Balfour the previous month. His rise through the ranks of the party was largely due to his stance on the issue of tariff reform – the taxation of goods imported into Britain – which had grown out of a need to cover costs from the Second Boer War (1899-1902). His first major speech on the matter in April 1902 was well received and earned him the position of Parliamentary Secretary to the Board of Trade in July 1902. The Conservative Party became increasingly divided between the 'Free Fooders' – those who supported free trade – and tariff reformers. The rift forced Balfour to resign in December 1905 and, with the Conservatives in opposition, Bonar Law became the principal spokesman for tariff reform in the shadow cabinet. His business experience and skill as a clear and concise speaker on economics cemented his importance to the party and, though the Conservatives lost the General Election of 1910, led to his becoming Leader of the Party.

However, by the start of 1913, the ongoing debate on tariff reform threatened to end Bonar Law's leadership prematurely. Heading into the 1910 General Election, the Conservatives had promised to submit tariff reform to a referendum, which became known as 'Bonar Law's Proposal'. In November 1912, the Conservatives withdrew this pledge, claiming that the government's failure to submit Home Rule to a Referendum rendered their own pledge null and void. This angered sections of the party, and after weeks of receiving negative letters about the change, Law outlined that he would not be averse to a return to the original policy, but it would require his resignation. In January 1913, with Bonar Law threatening his resignation if dissenting party members did not fall in line, a compromise over the tariff reform policy was agreed ensuring that he remained as Leader.

In Beerbohm's cartoon, Bonar Law can be seen arm in arm with Tariff Reform, as he was for much of his career. This suggests the way in which the issue had destabilised not only his own position as leader, but the party as a whole.

The note on Cold Shouldered Yet *is written by Alexander Beetles.*

29

COLD-SHOULDERED YET

MR BONAR LAW (TO TARIFF REFORM) 'IT'S A QUEE-ER THING, LADDIE, BUT THERE'S EVIDENTLY A SOR'RT OF A SOMEWHAT ABOUT YE THAT DOES NOT INSPIRE CONFIDENCE.'
Signed, inscribed with title and dated 1913
Pen ink, pencil and watercolour
12 x 15 ¾ inches
Provenance: The Jeffrey Archer Political Cartoon Collection
Illustrated: Max Beerbohm, *Fifty Caricatures*, New York:
E P Dutton& Company, 1913
Literature: Rupert Hart-Davis, *A Catalogue of the Caricatures of Max Beerbohm*, London: Macmillan, 1972, No 903
Exhibited: Leicester Galleries, 1913

Cold-Shouldered Yet.

Mr. Bonar Law (to Tariff Reform): "It's a queerer thing, laddie, but there's evidently a sort of a somewhat about ye that dinna inspire confidence."

Max
1914

Colonel Repington

As the military correspondent for *The Times* during the First World War, Charles à Court Repington (1858-1925) was the most significant and important military journalist of the period. Extravagant and self-important, he referred to himself as 'the most brilliant military writer of his day' in his own epitaph. Repington was extremely well-connected, and his reporting influenced decisions at the very highest level, to the extent that he was sometimes referred to as 'the twenty-third member of the cabinet'. In 1914, he had been the first to champion the appointment of Field Marshall Kitchener as Secretary of State for War, and the following year his reporting of the 'shell scandal', the shortage of artillery ammunition at the front, helped bring David Lloyd George to the position of Minister of Munitions. In 1918, the year of Max Beerbohm's caricature, Repington was sacked by *The Times* when the editor, Geoffrey Dawson, became exasperated with his continued stand against the War Cabinet.

In addition to his status as a formidable and influential journalist, Repington had also earned a reputation as a cad and a womaniser. A promising military career, during which he had been promoted to lieutenant-colonel and appointed CMG (Companion of the Order of St Michael and St George), had been cut short when a long-running affair with a married woman became public and forced his resignation in 1902. Though he blamed sabotage by a jealous rival, similar stories followed him throughout his journalistic career, as he became known as 'the playboy of the Western Front' and 'the gorgeous Wreckington'.

The note on Colonel Repington *is written by Alexander Beetles.*

30 (opposite)
COLONEL REPINGTON
Signed, inscribed with title and dated 1908
Watercolour and pencil
11 ¾ x 9 inches
Provenance: Sir Edward Maufe RA
Literature: Rupert Hart-Davis, *A Catalogue of the Caricatures of Max Beerbohm*, London: Macmillan, 1972, No 1216
Exhibited: Leicester Galleries, London, 1957

LAWSON WOOD
Clarence Lawson Wood, RI (1878-1957)

Lawson Wood was an accomplished cartoonist, illustrator and poster designer. He gained great popularity with his humorous illustrations of animals, including dinosaurs and monkeys. The ginger ape, Gran'pop, proved a particular favourite on both sides of the Atlantic.

Lawson Wood was born at 66 Woodsome Road, Dartmouth Park, London, on 23 August 1878, into a notably artistic family. He was the eldest child of the landscapist, Lewis Pinhorn Wood, and his wife, Louisa (née Watson), and the grandson of the architectural painter and printmaker, Lewis John Wood. He grew up with his family at Burnside, Shere, near Guildford, Surrey, and later at 51 Homefield Road, Chiswick, and was privately educated.

Wood received lessons in art from his father before studying intermittently in London at the Slade School of Art, under Fred Brown and Henry Tonks, and then at Heatherley's School of Fine Art. He also attended evening classes at Frank Calderon's School of Animal Painting, Kensington.

In 1896, at the age of 18, Wood joined the periodical publisher, C Arthur Pearson, working there for six years and eventually becoming its chief staff artist. While there, he met his future wife, the fashion artist, Charlotte Forge. They married in 1903, settled at Bedford Park, and had three children. The youngest was born in 1911, after the family had moved to 15 Albert Road, Bexhill, Sussex. In the following year, they settled at Court Lodge, Groombridge, near Tunbridge Wells, Kent. This was an untenanted mediaeval manor house that Wood had decided to transfer from its original position in Udimore, Sussex, engaging the architect, John D Clarke, and the historian, J E Ray, to supervise the operation.

Working in a freelance capacity from 1902, Wood became an accomplished poster designer and drew cartoons for a number of periodicals, including *The Bystander, Fry's Magazine, The Graphic, Nash's Magazine, Punch* and *The Strand Magazine*.

Among a range of subjects, he developed E T Reed's novel idea of using prehistory as a subject for humour, in such series as *Prehistoric Proverbs* (published in volume form in 1907). He showed examples of his comic work, in 1906, in a joint exhibition, held, with his father and grandfather, at the Modern Gallery, London, and then, in 1908, at a solo show at the Brook Street Art Gallery. A close friend of the cartoonist, Tom Browne, he joined him briefly as a member of the London Sketch Club.

Wood also produced more serious work, which he showed as a member of both the Royal Institute of Painters in Water Colours and the Old Dudley Art Society (becoming Vice President of the latter).

In 1915, a year after the outbreak of the First World War, Wood volunteered and, following training for the Army Service Corps at Aldershot, obtained a commission. Soon after, he became an officer in the Kite Balloon Wing of the Royal Flying Corps. During the battle of Vimy Ridge in April 1917, he sat high above the action and helped the allied artillery spot German strongholds. As a result, the French decorated him for his gallantry.

Despite active service, Wood still found time, in 1916, to set up a toy company in collaboration with his architect friend, John D Clarke, at premises in Commercial Road, Eastbourne. Made to his own designs, the toys became known as 'Lawson Woodies'. In the same year, the publisher, Frederick Warne, also launched him as a writer and illustrator of children's books, with the 'Mr' series.

Following the end of the war, Wood and his family settled at Old Tokefield, Cranleigh, Surrey, a house that his friend John D Clarke created out of three cottages. The village had become something of a colony of illustrators, providing as it did at various times a home to Stephen Baghot De La Bere, Edmund Dulac, Bertram Prance and William Heath Robinson. Like Robinson, he contributed to Percy Bradshaw's series of publications, 'The Art of the Illustrator', and also worked as a tutor for Percy Bradshaw's correspondence course, the Press Art School.

Wood collaborated briefly on cartoons with Keith Sholto Douglas, under the joint name of 'Hustlebuck'. Douglas's first wife, Josephine, worked as Wood's secretary (and she gave birth to Douglas's son, also called Keith, who became the most noted English poet of the Second World War). Douglas's second wife, whom he married in 1941, was Wood's daughter, Phoebe.

In 1923, Wood sold Old Tokefield to the novelist, Frank Swinnerton, and left Cranleigh, probably for Eastbourne, which certainly became his home by 1928. It seems that his wife, Charlotte, filed for divorce in 1929. During the following decade, he became a good friend of Ethel Webb, who lived at East Dean, just to the west of Eastbourne. Together, they created a sanctuary for badly treated horses, and this contributed to Wood's election as a Fellow of the Zoological Society in 1934. His work was always based on close observation of animal appearance and behaviour, which was informed by visits to London Zoo and the local zoo at Wannock Gardens, Polegate, and also by the animals in his own small menagerie.

Already famous, Wood gained international popularity with his humorous illustrations of animals, and especially the ginger ape, Gran'pop, who made his first appearance in *The Sketch* in 1932. He mounted solo shows of his comic art across Britain and, holding strict control over his copyright, sold reproductions of his images throughout the world. He became so successful in America that, in 1939, the animator, Ub Iwerks, who had helped Walt Disney to create Mickey Mouse, planned to produce 24 cartoon films featuring Gran'pop; however, the project was interrupted by the Second World War, and only three were completed.

Wood was already living with Ethel Webb at Ringwood Farm Cottages, East Dean, when, in 1942, his own house, in central Eastbourne, was destroyed by enemy bombing. Following the end of the war, he continued to publish cartoons and illustrations, including those that appeared in Dean's *Gran'pop's Annual*, published by Dean (1935-50), and books published by Birn Brothers (mostly 1946).

Towards the end of his life, Wood retired to Sidmouth, Devon, settling on the edge of the town at Downlands, Salcombe Hill. After a long illness, he died at his home on 26 October 1957.

Further reading

A E Johnson, *Lawson Wood* (Brush, Pen and Pencil Series), London: A & C Black, 1910;
John Jensen, 'Wood, (Clarence) Lawson (1878-1957)', H C G Matthew and Brian Harrison (eds), *Oxford Dictionary of National Biography*, Oxford University Press, 2018,
https://doi.org/10.1093/odnb/9780198614128.013.66128

31
GRAN'POP FEELS THE COLD SNAP
Signed
Watercolour with bodycolour
15 x 11 ½ inches
Exhibited: 'The Age of William Heath Robinson', West House, Pinner, April-May 2013, No 47

Gran'pop

Making his first appearance in *The Sketch* in 1932, Lawson Wood's ginger-coloured ape, Gran'pop, became one of the most popular cartoon characters on both sides of the Atlantic during the period between the two world wars. Wood was probably inspired in his creation of Gran'pop by George Studdy, who had launched the similarly popular puppy, Bonzo, in *The Sketch* a decade earlier.

Gran'pop is an elderly ape who, despite his age, still engages in a wide range of entertaining and energetic escapades with a cast of other animal characters. Most notably, these include younger monkeys – possibly Gran'pop's actual grandchildren – and also pigs. Gran'pop and his coterie clearly remain animals, and their characterisation is founded on Lawson Wood's acknowledged observation of animal appearance and behaviour. However, they use manmade – if makeshift – accessories, and mimic a wide range of human activities encompassing work, leisure and domestic life. The act of mimicry and the outcome of the activities both provide many opportunities for humour.

While appearing regularly in *The Sketch*, Wood's Gran'pop drawings soon graced the cover of the American magazine, *Collier's*, thanks to the efforts of the artist's hardworking agents, Francis & Mills. In *They Make Us Smile* (1942), the illustrator, Percy Bradshaw explained the expensive process by which such magazines as *Collier's* ordered these drawings: 'Publishers in America have indulged in transatlantic phone calls, at £5 a minute to order "Gran'pops", after which a "Gran'pop" sketch was transmitted by "telephotography", the finished drawing commissioned by cable and the completed picture dispatched a day or so later on the Queen Mary' (quoted in Jensen, 2018).

While *The Sketch* and *Collier's* were aimed at adults, Gran'pop soon began to be marketed to children, with the publication of Dean's *Gran'Pop's Annual* from 1935, and then other picture books. The ape also appeared in a variety of two-dimensional forms, on cigarette cards, postcards and prints. Many of these were published in languages other than English, including Danish, Dutch and German.

The famous American animator, Ub Iwerks, got Gran'pop moving, in three cartoon films in 1940, and the Shropshire company, Merrythought Toys transformed him into three-dimensions in 1938. Though the popularity of Gran'pop began to wane after the Second World War, Merrythought continued to produce soft toy versions of the character until 1964, almost a decade after the death of his creator.

(Detail of **33**)

32 (opposite)
IT'S SURPRISING WHAT IT CAN DO
Signed
Inscribed with title on reverse
Watercolour and bodycolour
15 ¼ x 12 inches

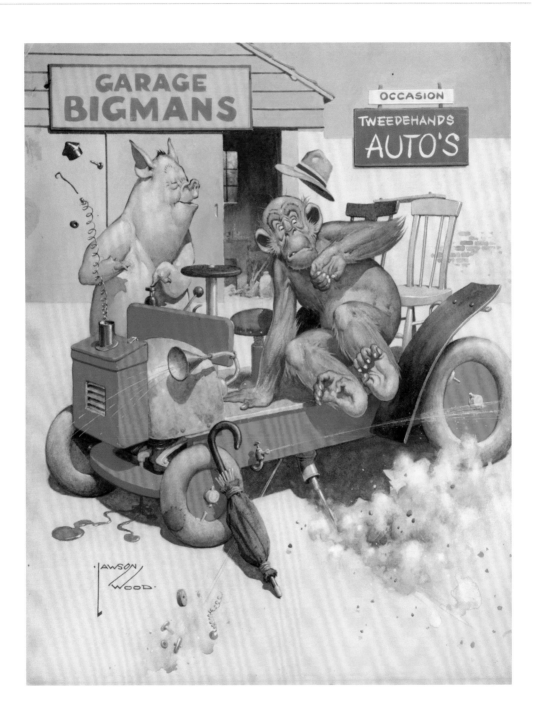

33
I HEARD THAT ONE AT
THE CLUB
Signed
Inscribed with title on reverse
Watercolour with bodycolour
14 ½ x 11 ¼ inches
Illustrated: Published as a print
by Forman, 1930

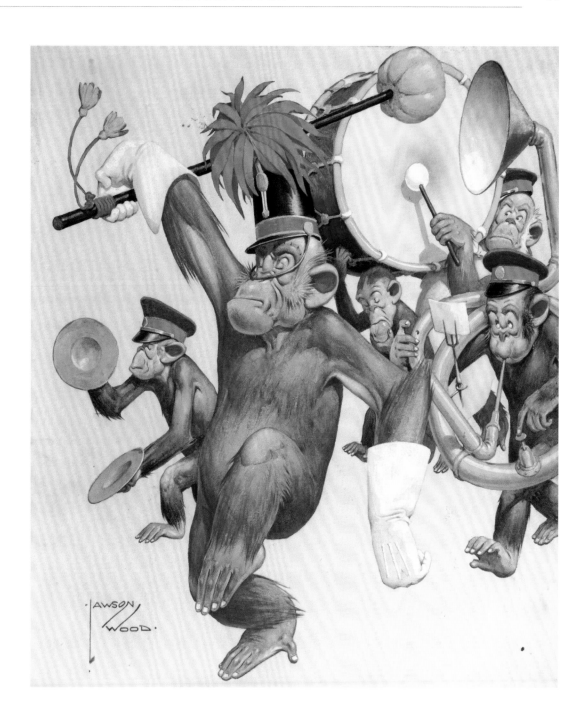

34
MONKEY BAND
Signed
Watercolour and
bodycolour
15 x 12 inches

35
THE 19TH 'HOLE'
Signed
Inscribed with title and 'Gran'pop
sticks to the old rules' on reverse
Watercolour and bodycolour
with pencil on board
14 ½ x 11 inches
Illustrated: Design for a postcard
for the 'Gran'pop' series
Exhibited: 'Hole in One!', The
Atkinson Gallery Southport,
May-August 2017

36
GRAN'POP AT IT AGAIN
YOU SAY YOUR ASSETS
HAVE SHRUNK?
Signed
Inscribed with title on reverse
Watercolour and bodycolour
15 ¼ x 12 inches

37
GRAN'POP AT IT AGAIN
WE'RE DOING BIG BUSINESS
Signed
Inscribed with title on reverse
Watercolour and bodycolour
15 x ¼ x 12 inches
Illustrated: Design for postcard
No 1650, for Valentine's of
Dundee;
Illustrated: *Marking Time with
Gran'Pop*, 1948 Calendar
for Melody Amusements,
Portland, Oregon

38
GRAN'POP AT IT AGAIN
THE BEST SERVICE GOING
Signed
Inscribed with title on reverse
Watercolour and bodycolour
15 ¼ x 12 inches

H M BATEMAN
Henry Mayo Bateman (1887-1970)

H M Bateman established his inimitable style before the First World War when, as he put it, he 'went mad on paper', by drawing people's mood and character. This culminated in 'The Man Who ...', his famous series of cartoons dramatising social gaffes.

H M Bateman was born at Sutton Forest in New South Wales, Australia, on 15 February 1887. He was the son of an Englishman who owned an export and packing business. A year after his birth, the family returned to England, and he was educated at Forest Hill House, South London. Given the freedom to develop his artistic leaning from an early age, he attended Westminster School of Art and Goldsmiths' College and, influenced by *Comic Cuts* and *Ally Sloper's Half-Holiday*, made contributions to *Scraps* (1903) and *The Tatler* (1904). He was encouraged by Phil May and John Hassall to spend some time in the studio of Charles van Havermaet at the New Art School, Stratford Studios, Kensington (1904-7). He also took up amateur boxing, tap-dancing, golf and fishing, hobbies that were to prove valuable as sources for cartoon material. He developed his inimitable style around 1911 when, as he put it, he 'went mad on paper' by drawing people's mood and character rather than their physical appearance. Many of his early caricatures show the influence of Sidney Sime and Henry Ospovat, and similarly depict musical and music-hall personalities and theatrical productions. He illustrated theatrical reviews in *The Bystander* (1910) and, as 'Our Untamed Artist at the Play', in *The Sketch* (1912-14). This work met with such success that he was also commissioned to produce posters for two plays by George Bernard Shaw, *Fanny's First Play* and *John Bull's Other Island* (both 1912). In the years before the First World War, he lived in South Clapham. During the war, he joined a London regiment, but was soon discharged on the grounds of ill health.

The beginning of the post-war period was marked by solo shows of Bateman's work at the Leicester Galleries (1919, 1921). It also saw the emergence of his famous series of cartoons concerning the social gaffe, 'The Man Who ...', while he also developed a sequential approach derived from Caran d'Ache and the cinema. Throughout his career he contributed to almost all the leading periodicals and illustrated a number of books. His art proved to be a breath of fresh air to the stuffy pages of *Punch*, and his vigorous, wholly visual approach was closer to continental work such as that of the German satirical magazine, *Simplicissimus*, than to anything in England. At the peak of his career in the 1930s, he was earning between four and five thousand pounds from cartoons for magazines, including *The Radio Times*, book illustrations and advertising. He drove the latest cars and, in 1925, built a house at Reigate Heath in Surrey. Following his retirement in 1939, he shared his time between Sampford Courtenay, Devon, and the Mediterranean island of Gozo. In 1962, the Fine Art Society mounted a retrospective of his work. He died on Gozo on 11 February 1970.

His work is represented in numerous public collections, including the British Museum.

Further reading
Anthony Anderson, *The Man Who Was H M Bateman*, Exeter: Webb & Bower, 1982; John Jensen, 'Bateman, Henry Mayo (1887-1970)', H C G Matthew and Brian Harrison (eds), *Oxford Dictionary of National Biography*, Oxford University Press, 2004, vol 4, pages 299-301

39
THE GENIUS WHO WAS QUITE HUMAN
Signed and dated 1916
Pen ink and watercolour
16 ½ x 8 ½ inches
Illustrated: H M Bateman, *More Drawings*,
London: Methuen & Co, 1922

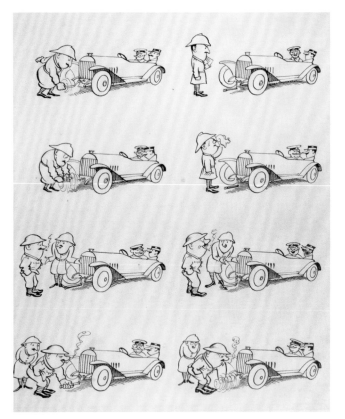
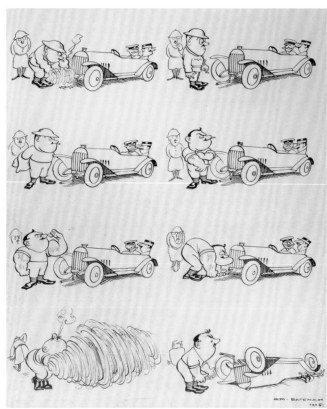

40
STIFF!
Signed and dated 1918
Inscribed with title below mount
Pen and ink with pencil
14 x 20 ¾ inches
Illustrated: *The Illustrated Sporting
& Dramatic News*, 2 October
1918, Page 235

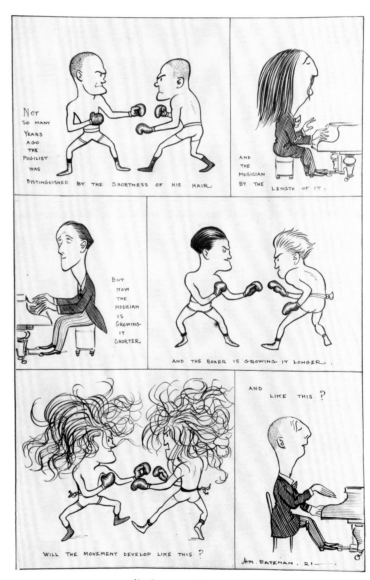

41
CONVERSATIONS
(THE COSTERS)
Signed and dated 1922
Inscribed 'Costers'
below mount
Pen and ink
10 x 8 inches

42
HAIR AND ART
Signed, inscribed with title
and dated 21
Pen and ink
13 ¾ x 9 inches
Illustrated: *Punch*, Summer
Number, 1921

43
SOULFUL
Signed and dated 23
Inscribed 'Soulfull' below mount
Pen ink and watercolour
14 ¾ x 10 ¾ inches

44
THE INCOME TAX OFFICIAL
ON THE ICE (OR CUTS A
FEW FIGURES)
Signed
Inscribed with title below mount
Pen ink and watercolour
14 ¼ x 10 inches
Illustrated: *The Tatler*;
H M Bateman, *Brought Forward:
A Further Collection of Drawings*,
London: Methuen & Co, 1931,
Page 63

PONT
Gavin Graham Laidler, ARIBA (1908-1940), known as 'Pont'

Following in the *Punch* tradition of George Du Maurier and Frank
Reynolds, Graham 'Pont' Laidler excelled at satirising the British
middle classes. Before his premature death at the age of just 32,
Laidler had established a reputation as one of the finest
cartoonists of the twentieth-century with his acute observations
of the 'British Character'.

For biography of Pont, please refer to *The Illustrators*, 2014, page 130.

45
THE BRITISH CHARACTER
FAILURE TO APPRECIATE GOOD MUSIC
Signed
Inscribed with title on reverse
Pen and ink with pencil
7 ½ x 10 ¾ inches
Illustrated: Pont, *The British Character Studied and Revealed*,
London: Collins, 1938, Page 29

3 William
Heath Robinson

WILLIAM HEATH ROBINSON

William Heath Robinson (1872-1944)

Heath Robinson is a household name, and a byword for a design or construction that is 'ingeniously or ridiculously over-complicated' (as defined by *The New Oxford Dictionary of English*, 1998, page 848). Yet, he was also a highly distinctive and versatile illustrator, whose work could touch at one extreme the romantic watercolours of a Dulac or Rackham, at another the sinister grotesqueries of a Peake, and at yet another the eccentricities of an Emett.

For a biography of William Heath Robinson, please refer to *The Illustrators*, 2018, page 22.

Essays on various aspects of Heath Robinson's achievements have appeared in previous editions of *The Illustrators*: on his illustrations to Rabelais in 1996, pages 112-113; on the relationship of his illustrations to those of Arthur Rackham in 1997, pages 124-125; on his illustrations to *The Arabian Nights Entertainments* in 1999, pages 73-74; and on one of his illustrations to *Twelfth Night* in 2000, pages 17-18.

The Chris Beetles Gallery has mounted a number of significant exhibitions of the work of William Heath Robinson, including:

1. 'William Heath Robinson (1872-1944)', Chris Beetles Gallery, March 1987 (with a fully illustrated catalogue)

2. 'The Brothers Robinson', Chris Beetles Gallery and the Royal Festival Hall, February 1992 (with a fully illustrated catalogue – see catalogue image)

3. 'William Heath Robinson (1872-1944). 50th Anniversary Exhibition', Chris Beetles Gallery, September 1994

4. 'The Gadget King', Manchester City Art Galleries, Heaton Hall, May-October 2000

5. 'W Heath Robinson', Dulwich Picture Gallery, Linbury Room, November 2003 (to complement Dulwich's own exhibition of William Heath Robinson)

6. 'Heath Robinson at Nunnington Hall', National Trust, Nunnington Hall, North Yorkshire, July 2005

7. 'Contraptions. William Heath Robinson (1872-1944)', Chris Beetles Gallery, June-August 2007 (to launch a volume of cartoons published by Duckworth)

8. 'William Heath Robinson 1872-1944', Chris Beetles Gallery, May-June 2011 (with a fully illustrated catalogue– see catalogue image)

9. 'The Inventive Art of William Heath Robinson', Chris Beetles Gallery, March-April 2016

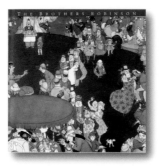

Geoffrey Beare, *The Brothers Robinson*, London: Chris Beetles Ltd, 1992 Fully illustrated catalogue, hardback, limited to 500 copies, 240 pages

Geoffrey Beare, *William Heath Robinson*, London: Chris Beetles, 2011 Fully illustrated catalogue, paperback, 163 pages

The Bystander
on Golf

46

PUTTING OUT THE OLD HOLED OUT

Signed
Inscribed 'Holed Out'
below mount
Pen and ink
14 ¾ x 10 ¾ inches
Illustrated: *The Bystander*,
3 January 1923, Page 31
Exhibited: 'William Heath
Robinson 1872-1944',
Chris Beetles Gallery,
May- June 2011, No 174;
'Hole in One!', The Atkinson
Gallery, Southport,
May-August 2017

This cartoon was published in
The Bystander to mark the
turning of the year from 1922 to
1923, with '1922' written on the
ball. The date was subsequently
altered by the artist.

THE KIND CADDY-BIRD OF
ST. ANDREWS

47
THE KINDLY CADDY-BIRD
OF ST ANDREWS
PURSUING ITS DAILY
ROUND
Signed and inscribed 'The Kind
Caddy-Bird of St Andrews'
and 'Bystander'
Pen ink and watercolour
16 x 11 ¼ inches
Illustrated: *The Bystander*,
6 February 1924, Page 305
Exhibited: 'William Heath
Robinson 1872-1944',
Chris Beetles Gallery, May- June
2011, No 178;
'Hole in One!', The Atkinson
Gallery, Southport,
May-August 2017

48
CASABIANCA OF
THE LINKS
Signed and inscribed with title
Watercolour with pen and ink
15 x 10 ¾ inches
Illustrated: *The Bystander*,
11 March 1925, Page 553
Exhibited: 'The Gadget King',
Manchester City Art Galleries,
Heaton Hall, May-October 2000;
'William Heath Robinson
1872-1944', Chris Beetles
Gallery, May-June 2011, No 180;
'Hole in One!', The Atkinson
Gallery, Southport,
May-August 2017

CASABIANCA OF THE LINKS

A TRAINED EARLY BIRD COMPELLING A WORM TO
TURN BEFORE IT CASTS

49
A TRAINED EARLY BIRD
COMPELLING A WORM TO
TURN BEFORE IT CASTS
Signed, inscribed with title
and 'For the preservation of
our greens'
Pen and ink with pencil
14 ¾ x 10 ¾ inches
Illustrated: *The Bystander*,
18 April 1923, Page 29
Exhibited: 'William Heath
Robinson 1872-1944',
Chris Beetles Gallery, May-June
2011, No 170;
'Hole in One!', The Atkinson
Gallery, Southport,
May-August 2017

50
SUMMER TROUBLES IN
THE TROPICS – SNAKE
CASTS ON THE SAHARA
GOLF COURSE
Signed and inscribed with title
and 'Bystander Summer No'
Pen ink and watercolour
15 ½ x 11 ½ inches
Illustrated: *The Bystander*,
20 June 1923, Page 121
Exhibited: 'The Gadget King',
Manchester City Art Galleries,
Heaton Hall, May-October 2000;
'William Heath Robinson
1872-1944', Chris Beetles
Gallery, May- June 2011, No 171

SUMMER TROUBLES IN THE TROPICS
SNAKE CASTS ON THE SAHARA GOLF COURSE

INCURABLE

51
THE INCURABLE GOLFER
DOES A SHORT HOLE
IN ONE
Signed
Inscribed 'incurable' below mount
Pen ink and watercolour
17 x 12 inches
Illustrated: *The Humorist*,
3 October 1931, Page 275
Exhibited: 'William Heath
Robinson 1872-1944',
Chris Beetles Gallery,
May-June 2011, No 185;
'Hole in One!', The Atkinson
Gallery Southport,
20 May - 28 August 2017

ALL IS NOT GOLD THAT GLITTERS

AMERICAN GOLFERS, WHO THINK
THEY SEE A BOTTLE OF WHISKEY,
OVERCOME WITH HORROR AND AVERSION

W. HEATH ROBINSON

52

**ALL IS NOT GOLD
THAT GLITTERS**

AMERICAN GOLFERS, WHO
THINK THEY SEE A BOTTLE OF
WHISKEY, OVERCOME WITH
HONOUR AND AVERSION

Signed and inscribed with title

Pen and ink

16 x 11 inches

Illustrated: *The Bystander*,
15 August 1923, Page 633

Exhibited: 'William Heath
Robinson 1872-1944',
Chris Beetles Gallery, May-June
2011, No 175;
'Hole in One!', The Atkinson
Gallery, Southport,
May-August 2017

AN UNFORTUNATE BACK-HANDER
AT ST ANDREWS

53
AN UNFORTUNATE
BACK-HANDER AT ST ANDREWS
Signed and inscribed with title
Pen ink and crayon
15 ¼ x 10 ¾ inches
Illustrated: *The Bystander*,
22 August 1923, Page 697
Exhibited: 'William Heath Robinson
1872-1944', Chris Beetles Gallery,
May-June 2011, No 173;
'Hole in One!', The Atkinson Gallery,
Southport, May-August 2017

54

KNOCKING THE GROUND FROM BENEATH HIS FEET

THE TOO VIGOROUS GOLFER: 'NOW I HAVE JUST ABOUT CUT MYSELF OFF'

Signed and inscribed with title and 'Bystander'

Pen ink and watercolour

14 ½ x 10 ¾ inches

Illustrated: *The Bystander*, 7 November 1923, Page 397

Exhibited: 'William Heath Robinson 1872-1944', Chris Beetles Gallery, May-June 2011, No 176; 'Hole in One!', The Atkinson Gallery, Southport, May-August 2017

KNOCKING THE GROUND FROM BENEATH HIS FEET
THE TOO VIGOROUS GOLFER – *Now I have just about cut myself off.*

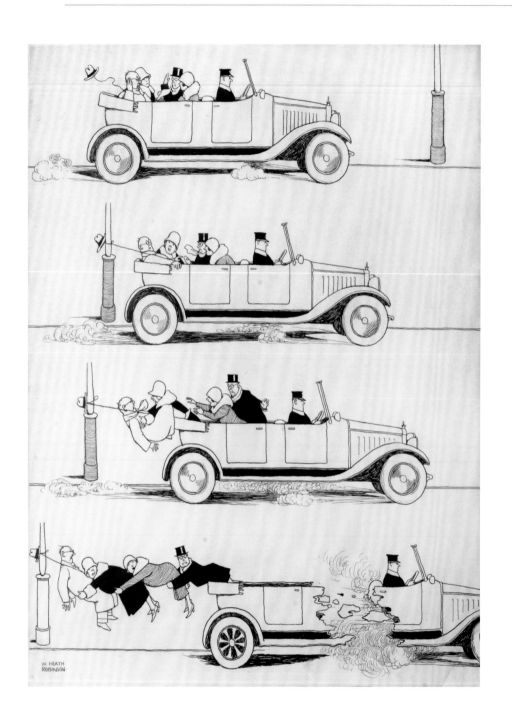

55
ANOTHER
INSTANCE OF THE
UNRELIABILITY OF A
CHEAP CAR IN AN
EMERGENCY
Signed
Pen and ink
17 ½ x 13 ½ inches

How to Live in a Flat

Nos **56-60** are all illustrated in
W H Robinson and K R G
Browne, *How To Live in a Flat*,
London: Hutchinson & Co, 1936

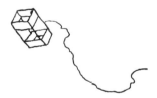

56
PETS' PLAY-GROUND, TRYPLIT
MANSIONS, MAIDA VALE
Inscribed with title
Pen and ink
11 ½ x 7 ¾ inches
Illustrated: Page 47
Exhibited: 'The Gadget King',
Manchester City Art Galleries,
Heaton Hall, May-October 2000;
'William Heath Robinson 1872-1944',
Chris Beetles Gallery, May-June 2011,
No 56

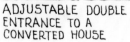

ADJUSTABLE DOUBLE
ENTRANCE TO A
CONVERTED HOUSE

58 (opposite)
A FLAT WEDDING
Inscribed with title
Pen and ink
10 ½ x 7 ½ inches
Illustrated: Page 7
Exhibited: 'William Heath
Robinson 1872-1944',
Chris Beetles Gallery,
May-June 2011, No 52;
'The Age of William Heath
Robinson', West House, Pinner,
April-May 2013, No 7

57
ADJUSTABLE DOUBLE
ENTRANCE TO A
CONVERTED HOUSE
Inscribed with title
Pen and ink
9 x 7 ¾ inches
Illustrated: Pages 78-79
Exhibited: 'Heath Robinson.
Machines and Inventions', The
West House & Heath Robinson
Museum Trust, Pinner,
March-April 2011, No 27

A FLAT WEDDING

AN 'AIR FRAIS' BUNGALOW FOR WARM WEATHER

HOW TO DO WITHOUT THE MANTELSHELF IN A MODERN FLAT

59
AN 'FRAIS' BUNGALOW
FOR WARM WEATHER
Inscribed with title
Pen and ink
7 x 7 ½ inches
Illustrated: Page 105
Exhibited: 'Heath Robinson.
Machines and Inventions', The
West House & Heath Robinson
Museum Trust, Pinner,
March-April 2011, No 30;
'Comedy and Commentary',
Mottisfont, January-April 2020

60
HOW TO DO WITHOUT
THE MANTEL SHELF IN A
MODERN FLAT
Inscribed with title
Pen and ink
5 ¼ x 5 ½ inches
Illustrated: Page 19
Exhibited: 'William Heath Robinson
1872-1944', Chris Beetles Gallery,
May-June 2011, No 54;
'The Inventive Art of William
Heath Robinson', Chris Beetles
Gallery, March-April 2016

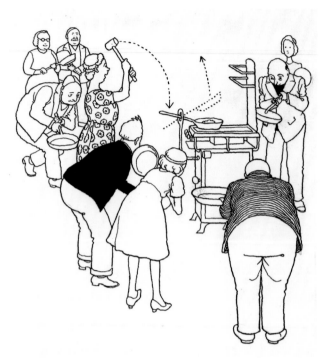

REVIVAL OF THE
TIME HONOURED RITE
OF TOSSING THE
PANCAKE ON SHROVE
TUESDAY

THE MONTHLY
OVERHAUL

How to Run a Communal Home

61
REVIVAL OF THE TIME-HONOURED RITE OF TOSSING
THE PANCAKE ON SHROVE TUESDAY
Inscribed with title
Pen and ink
6 ½ x 5 ½ inches
Illustrated: W Heath Robinson and Cecil Hunt, *How To Run a Communal Home*, London: Hutchinson & Co, 1943, Page 72, 'Rites and Ceremonies'
Exhibited: 'Heath Robinson, Machines and Inventions', The West House & Heath Robinson Museum Trust, Pinner, March-April 2011, No 46; 'William Heath Robinson 1872-1944', Chris Beetles Gallery, May-June 2011, No 102

62
THE MONTHLY OVERHAUL
Inscribed with title
Pen and ink
6 ½ x 5 ½ inches
Illustrated: W Heath Robinson and Cecil Hunt, *How To Run a Communal Home*, London: Hutchinson & Co, 1943, Page 98, 'Anno Domini'
Exhibited: 'The Inventive Art of William Heath Robinson', Chris Beetles Gallery, March-April 2016

4 E H Shepard

E H SHEPARD
Ernest Howard Shepard, MC OBE (1879-1976)

While E H Shepard is now best remembered for his immortal illustrations to *Winnie-the-Pooh* and *The Wind in the Willows*, he was a wide-ranging illustrator, with an unsurpassed genius for representing children, and an underrated talent for political cartoons.

For a biography of E H Shepard, please refer to *The Illustrators*, 2018, page 41.

For essays on various aspects of the artist's achievements, see *The Illustrators*, 1999, pages 151-152; *The Illustrators*, 2000, pages 28-32; and *The Illustrators*, 2007, pages 199-200.

63
A GENTLEMAN ... WAS FORCED TO RISE FROM TABLE
Signed
Inscribed 'A gentleman that was at dinner with my lord ... was forced to rise from table' below mount
Pen and ink on board
8 x 11 ¼ inches
Illustrated: O F Morshead (ed), *Everybody's Pepys: the Diary of Samuel Pepys 1660-1669*, London, Bell, 1926, Facing Page 21

64
THE TOWN MUSIQUE
Signed
Inscribed with title and 'Cambridge' below mount
Pen and ink
10 ¾ x 7 inches
Illustrated: O F Morshead (ed), *Everybody's Pepys: the Diary of Samuel Pepys 1660-1669*, London, Bell, 1926, Facing Page 436

65

SELINA A MAENAD
NOW HATLESS AND
TOSSING DISORDERED
LOCKS, STALKED
AROUND THE PYRE
Signed with initials
Signed, inscribed with title,
book title and artist's address
on reverse
Pen and ink
8 ¾ x 7 inches
Illustrated: Kenneth Grahame,
Dream Days, London: The Bodley
Head, 1930, Page 14

Shepard's approach to The Wind in the Willows

E H Shepard had a very high opinion of Kenneth Grahame's *The Wind in the Willows* (1908), and considered it 'one of the books – he had a mental list of them, he said – that should not be illustrated' (Rawle Knox (ed), *The Work of E H Shepard*, London: Methuen, 1979, page 178). However, when offered the job, he accepted it. He was excited at the chance to attempt it and was sure that he could do better than those who had tried before: Paul Branson (1913), Nancy Barnhart (1922) and Wyndham Payne (1927). Grahame was sceptical as to Shepard's suitability. But his own preferred choice, Arthur Rackham, had rejected the project when the book was first published, through pressure of work, and would not produce his own edition until 1940, after the author's death.

Shepard visited Grahame at Church Cottage, Pangbourne, Berkshire, in order to persuade him of his worth. Perhaps thinking of A A Milne's toys, Grahame told Shepard that 'my animals are not puppets; they always make them puppets', then added, as both plea and blessing, that 'I love these little people; be kind to them.' Unable to accompany Shepard down to the Thames, he,

> told me of the river near by, of the meadows where Mole broke ground that spring morning, of the banks where Rat had his house, of the pools where Otter hid, and of Wild Wood way up on the hill about the river.
> (E H Shepard, 'Illustrating *The Wind in the Willows*',

The Horn Book, April 1954)

Shepard then went out to look and sketch, 'and swore he could have seen Otter rising from the water, and Badger on the bank' (Knox, 1979, page 178). He left Grahame 'more excited at the prospect of that work than any other he had undertaken, in spite of its immense difficulty' (Knox, 1979, page 180). Grahame, in turn, was delighted with the results.

Peter Green has noticed how Grahame had transferred 'the scene of *The Wind in the Willows* … in his mind to the country and the riverside surrounding his new home' way upstream from its original setting. This subtle change has been perpetuated so potently by Shepard's illustrations 'that many people remain convinced to this day not only that Rat and Mole lived near Pangbourne, but that *The Wind in the Willows* was actually written there' (*Kenneth Grahame 1859-1932*, London: John Murray, 1959, page 346). As a result, Shepard, who was so cautious of interpreting Grahame's book, significantly increased the status of an already classic text.

66
MOLE AT HOME
Signed with initials
Pen and ink with bodycolour on board
4 ½ x 6 ¼ inches
Illustrated: Kenneth Grahame, *The Wind in the Willows*, London: Methuen & Co, 1931, Page 113

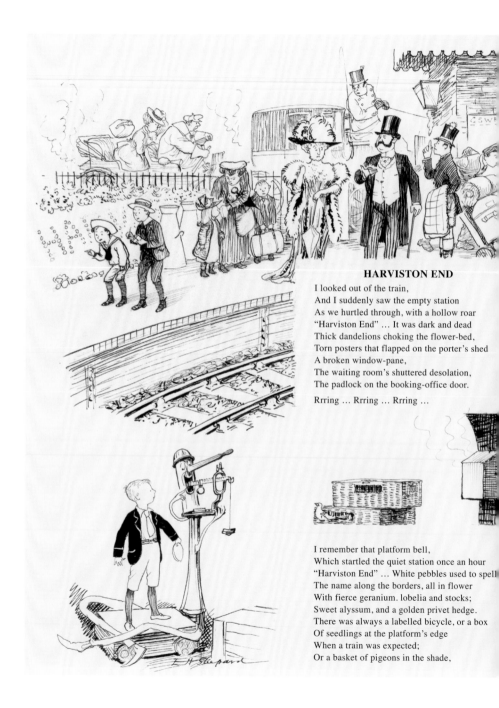

HARVISTON END

I looked out of the train,
And I suddenly saw the empty station
As we hurtled through, with a hollow roar
"Harviston End" … It was dark and dead
Thick dandelions choking the flower-bed,
Torn posters that flapped on the porter's shed
A broken window-pane,
The waiting room's shuttered desolation,
The padlock on the booking-office door.

Rrring … Rrring … Rrring …

I remember that platform bell,
Which startled the quiet station once an hour
"Harviston End" … White pebbles used to spell
The name along the borders, all in flower
With fierce geranium. lobelia and stocks;
Sweet alyssum, and a golden privet hedge.
There was always a labelled bicycle, or a box
Of seedlings at the platform's edge
When a train was expected;
Or a basket of pigeons in the shade,

Harviston End

'Harviston End' was written early in the career of Peter Ling (1926-2006), who is best remembered as the co-creator of the ITV soap opera, *Crossroads*.

Ling possibly wrote the poem as a response to the nationalisation of Britain's railways in 1948, and the subsequent closure of lines and stations. In the three years alone between nationalisation and the publication of the poem, almost 200 stations were closed. A more concerted programme of closures would occur following the implementation of British Rail's Modernisation Plan in 1955, eight years before Richard Beeching's infamous 1963 report, 'The Reshaping of Britain's Railways'.

Though Harviston End is a fictional station, its name chimes with that of one that closed in 1948 (Harringworth, Northamptonshire) and two that would close in 1951 (Hallington, Lincolnshire, and Harlington Halt, South Yorkshire).

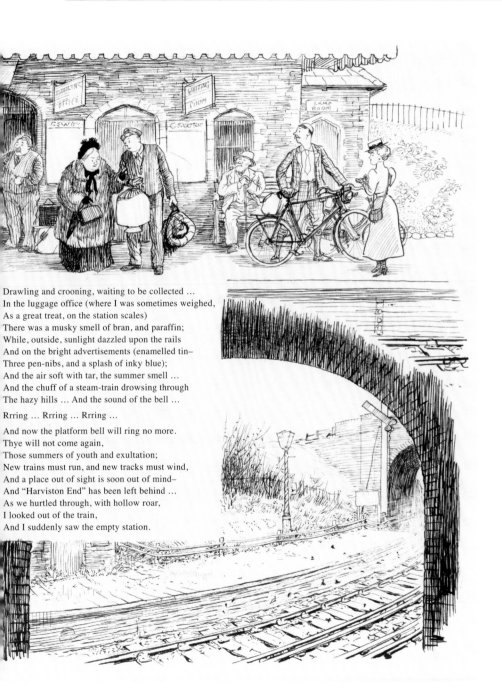

Drawling and crooning, waiting to be collected …
In the luggage office (where I was sometimes weighed,
As a great treat, on the station scales)
There was a musky smell of bran, and paraffin;
While, outside, sunlight dazzled upon the rails
And on the bright advertisements (enamelled tin–
Three pen-nibs, and a splash of inky blue);
And the air soft with tar, the summer smell …
And the chuff of a steam-train drowsing through
The hazy hills … And the sound of the bell …

Rrring … Rrring … Rrring …

And now the platform bell will ring no more.
Thye will not come again,
Those summers of youth and exultation;
New trains must run, and new tracks must wind,
And a place out of sight is soon out of mind–
And "Harviston End" has been left behind …
As we hurtled through, with hollow roar,
I looked out of the train,
And I suddenly saw the empty station.

Please note that the poem has been
added to show how it appeared in
Punch and is not part of the artwork.

67
HARVISTON END
Signed
Signed with the initials of Russell
Brockbank, *Punch*'s Art Editor,
below mount
Pen and ink on board
12 ½ x 18 ½ inches
Illustrated: *Punch*, 10 January 1951,
Pages 48-49, 'Harviston End' by Peter Ling

INCIDENT IN AUGUST

When the Cirle train was held up by a signal
Between Gloucester Road and High Street (Ken.)
In the battering dog-day heat of August
We sweated and mopped our brows. And then
We saw in the cutting, amid the loosestrife
And butterflies looping through bindweed trails,
A boy who lay drinking, straight from the bottle,
When of course, he was paid to look after the rails.

High stood the sun and the heat-haze shimmered,
The crickets shrilled to the burnished tracks;
But our minds and the motors throbbed together,
Insisting "You're late. You mustn't relax.
You mustn't look backward, you mustn't look ...
Southward?"
(Oh, the linemen stood by in the hills of Var
And leaned on their spades as the trains went past them
And swigged red wine from a great stone jar.)

Now, the boy in the sunlight was drinking water –
Or beer at the best. It might have been Beaune
Or Chateauneuf, but a London embankment
Was not the slopes of the Côtes-du-Rhône.
Still, a Mistral blew out of dry Vaucluse,
A Mistral blew over South-West Ten ...
Till the train pulled out from the Mondragon-sur-Lez
As the points changed back towards High Street
(Ken.)

Please note that the poem
has been added to show how
it appeared in *Punch* and is
not part of the artwork.

68
INCIDENT IN AUGUST
Signed and inscribed with title
Signed with the initials of
Kenneth Bird ('Fougasse'),
Punch's Art Editor below mount
Pen and ink on board
11 ½ x 9 ¾ inches
Illustrated: *Punch*, 27 August
1952, Page 285, 'Incident in
August' by Bryan Morgan

5 Mabel Lucie Attwell

MABEL LUCIE ATTWELL
Mabel Lucie Attwell, SWA (1879-1964)

Mabel Lucie Attwell developed her own imaginative, and often amusing, imagery through annuals and postcards. Then, as her popularity increased, she applied it to a wide range of products. She was a household name by the 1920s, by which time no home was complete without an Attwell plaque or money-box biscuit tin.

Mabel Lucie Attwell was born at 182 Mile End Road, London, on 4 June 1879, the sixth child of the butcher, Augustus Attwell, and his wife, Emily Ann (née Harris) . She was educated privately and at the Coopers' Company Coborn School, in the Bow Road, where she showed an early talent for art. She funded her own studies at Heatherley's and St Martin's School of Art (1895-1900), and, while at the latter, met fellow student, Harold Earnshaw, who would become a painter and illustrator. They married in 1908, and would have three children.

Disliking her formal training, Attwell completed neither course, and turned with some relief to contributions to periodicals and commissions for illustrated books, including several in Raphael Tuck's series, 'Raphael House Library of Gift Books' (1909-25), including a successful edition of *Alice in Wonderland* (1910). Her work as an illustrator was admired by Queen Mary of Romania, who invited her to stay at the royal palace in Bucharest and collaborated with her on two children's books, *Peeping Pansy* (1919) and *The Lost Princess* (1924). Influences on her work included her friend, Hilda Cowham, and such members of the London Sketch Club as John Hassall and William Heath Robinson.

After her husband lost his arm, through active service in the First World War, Attwell became the mainstay of the family. In 1922, she produced the first of her hugely successful children's annuals. Three years later, she was elected to the Society of Women Artists. A rapid and prolific worker, with a keen business sense, she also designed cards, posters, calendars, figurines and wall plaques, and saw her creations turned into crockery patterns and soft toys.

For most of her career, Attwell lived between London and Sussex with her husband, Harold Earnshaw. Following the deaths of their son, Brian (in 1935), and then of Harold (in 1937), and bomb damage to her two London homes (in 1940), she moved to Foxfold, Wiltshire. At the end of the Second World War, she settled in Fowey, Cornwall, with her son, Peter, as a companion, and remained there until her death on 5 November 1964. Her business was carried on by her daughter, Marjorie (known as Peggy).

Further reading

Brian Alderson (rev), 'Attwell [married name Earnshaw], Mabel Lucie (1879-1964)', H C G Matthew and Brian Harrison (eds), *Oxford Dictionary of National Biography*, Oxford University Press, 2004, vol 2, pages 885-887

Chris Beetles' biography of Mabel Lucie Attwell, published by Pavilion Books in 1985, sold out in hardback, and is now published in paperback by Chris Beetles Ltd.

69-76 are Provenance: The Estate of Mabel Lucie Attwell

69 (opposite)
YOU'RE SUCH A COMFORT TO ME!
Inscribed 'My Hot Water Bottle'
below mount
Pen and ink with pencil and bodycolour
on board
10 ¼ x 8 ¼ inches
Preliminary design for postcard No 2737,
for Valentine of Dundee, 1934

70
JUS' CRYIN' MYSELF TO SLEEP!
Signed
Watercolour and bodycolour with pencil
7 ½ x 11 ¼ inches
Illustrated: Design for postcard No 2037,
for Valentine of Dundee, 1931
Literature: John Henty, *The Collectable
World of Mabel Lucie Attwell*, London:
Richard Dennis, 1999, Page 56, as No 2037

71 (opposite)
IF I LEAVE A CANDLE
BURNING IN THE WINDOW
P'RAPS YOU'LL FIND THE
WAY BACK SOON – TO ME!
Watercolour and bodycolour with pencil
11 x 9 ¾ inches
Illustrated: Design for postcard No 1580,
for Valentine of Dundee, 1929
Literature: John Henty, *The Collectable
World of Mabel Lucie Attwell*, London:
Richard Dennis, 1999, Page 52,
as No 1580

72
OH! – LOOK AT ME LOOKING
AT YOU
Signed
Inscribed with title and 'You can't do that
here' on reverse
Watercolour with bodycolour on board
9 ½ x 8 ¼ inches
Illustrated: Design for postcard No 3281,
for Valentine of Dundee, 1936
Literature: John Henty, *The Collectable
World of Mabel Lucie Attwell*, London:
Richard Dennis, 1999, Page 63,
as No 3281

73
GET WELL QUICKLY!
Signed
Watercolour and bodycolour on board
9 x 7 inches
Illustrated: Design for postcard No 3531,
for Valentine of Dundee, 1936, with the
caption, 'I'm not "alarmed" – no – not a
bit/When my clock goes off –/I just smiles
at it!/That's why I'm sometimes late!'
Literature: John Henty, *The Collectable
World of Mabel Lucie Attwell*, London:
Richard Dennis, 1999, Page 64, as No 3531

74
'DOROTHY DEAR' –
'YOU CANNOT BE DOROTHY
DEAR – OH NO!'
Inscribed with title below mount
Pen and ink with pencil on board
7 x 10 inches

75
WITH LOVE – FROM ME
Signed
Inscribed with title and 'Postcard No: 5657'
on reverse
Pen ink and watercolour with bodycolour
and pencil
10 ¼ x 6 ½ inches
Illustrated: Design for postcard No 5657,
for Valentine of Dundee, 1957
Literature: John Henty, *The Collectable
World of Mabel Lucie Attwell*, London:
Richard Dennis, 1999, Page 114, as No 5657

TODAY WE'LL DO OUR GARDENING
TO HELP OUR FLOWERS TO GROW.
WE WATER THEM AND WEED THEM —
AND PLANT THEM IN A ROW.

TUESDAY

MABEL
LUCIE
ATTWELL

76
TODAY WE'LL DO OUR GARDENING
TO HELP OUR FLOWERS TO GROW.
WE WATER THEM AND WEED THEM —
AND PLANT THEM IN A ROW
Signed
Pen ink and watercolour
9 x 9 inches
Design for a Handkerchief

6 K F Barker

K F BARKER

Kathleen Frances Barker (1901-1963)

K F Barker was a sensitive and observant writer and illustrator
of books about animals, and especially dogs and horses.
In illustrating the work of other authors, she produced a fine edition of Anna Sewell's equestrian classic, *Black Beauty* (1936).

Kathleen Frances Barker was born at The Beeches, Wellow Road, Ollerton,
Nottinghamshire, on 2 January 1901, the third of four children of (John)
Wright Barker, the painter of hunting scenes and animal portraits, and his
wife, Ellen Mary (née Alcock). Probably at the outbreak of the First World
War, the family moved to Thorn Lea, 16 Duchy Road, Harrogate,
Yorkshire, and this would remain Kathleen's home for the remainder of her
life. Following in her father's footsteps, she produced images of animals, and
especially dogs, some of which she contributed to *The Field*, *Tailwagger* and
the *Yorkshire Evening Post*.

In 1933, Barker began to write and illustrate books, including those by
other authors, most of which were published by A & C Black, Country Life
and William Heinemann. Her work was informed by her love of animals
and her favourite pastimes: riding, otter hunting and beagling. Employing
pen, ink and pencil, she depicted her subjects with care and affection, often
concentrating on their appearance and behaviour to the exclusion of
extraneous setting or action. Though commissions dried up during the
Second World War, she renewed her literary activity in the 1950s, and has
four books published by George G Harrap, as well as others by Country
Life. She died in Harrogate on 1 April 1963.

77-84 were illustrated in
Anna Sewell, Black Beauty. The
Life Story of a Horse, London:
A & C Black, 1936

77
BLACK BEAUTY
IN BLINKERS
Pen ink and chalk with
bodycolour
4 ¼ x 3 ¼ inches
Illustrated: Spine of Dust Jacket

78
BLACK BEAUTY
Charcoal, chalk and bodycolour
12 x 10 ¾ inches
Illustrated: Front Cover of
Dust Jacket

Black Beauty

Originally published in 1877, Anna Sewell's *Black Beauty* was an innovative novel. It was one of the first to have an animal narrator, and was intended to draw the attention of an adult readership to equine cruelty and the need to prevent it. An immediate bestseller, it led to changes in the law in both Britain and the United States. Gradually, as its position as a campaigning novel lessened, it became considered a classic of children's literature.

79
BLACK BEAUTY
Signed
Pencil
12 ½ x 8 ½ inches
Illustrated: Frontispiece

80
EARLY DAYS WITH
MY MOTHER
Signed
Pencil
12 ½ x 8 ½ inches
Illustrated: Facing Page 4

81
THE CARTER WAS
SHOUTING AND FLOGGING
THE TWO HORSES
Signed
Pencil with pen and ink
10 ¾ x 14 ½ inches
Illustrated: Facing Page 96

82
THAT IS JUST LIKE THE STAR
BLACK BEAUTY HAD
Signed
Pencil and charcoal
12 x 10 ¾ inches
Illustrated: Facing Page 252

83
GINGER TROTTED ANXIOUSLY
ALONG BY THE HEDGE
Signed
Pencil
14 ½ x 10 ¾ inches
Illustrated: Facing Page 128

84
JUST TROT HIM OUT, WILL YOU?
Signed
Pencil with charcoal and bodycolour
12 x 10 ¾ inches
Illustrated: Facing Page 245

85-94 were illustrated in
K F Barker, *Nothing But Dogs*,
London: Adam & Charles
Black, 1938

85 (above left)
THY WAYS SHALL BE
MY WAYS
Inscribed with title, 'and thy gods
my gods' 'Section I' and '(Dogs as
Pals)' on a detached slip of paper
Pencil, 8 x 5 ¼ inches
Illustrated: Page 8

86 (above right)
PADDY,
AN IRISH SETTER
Inscribed with title, 'Section VII'
and 'Shooting-Dogs' on a
detached slip of paper
Pencil
13 x 9 ½ inches
Illustrated: Page 70

87 (left)
WIRE-HAIRED
FOX TERRIER
FROM NOSE TO STERN HE LOOKS
LIKE A GENTLEMAN
Signed and dated 1935
Pencil
8 x 9 inches
Illustrated: Page 61

88 (right)
A 'ONE-MAN SORT'.
DANDY DINMONT
Inscribed with title, 'Section I'
and '(Dogs as Pals)' on
detached slip of paper
Pencil
9 ½ x 7 inches
Illustrated: Page 11

89 (above)
POINTER
Inscribed with title, 'Section VII'
and '(Shooting-Dogs)' on a
detached slip of paper
Pencil
11 x 14 ½ inches
Illustrated: Page 79

90 (below)
ROUGH-COATED COLLIE
Inscribed with title, 'Section VIII'
and '(Sheep Dogs)' on a
detached slip of paper
Pencil
9 x 11 ½ inches
Illustrated: Page 80

91
THAT GRAND OLD BREED, THE ENGLISH MASTIFF
Inscribed with title, 'Section IX' and 'The Long & The Short of Them'
on a detached slip of paper
Pencil
11 ½ x 7 inches
Illustrated: Page 90

92 (below)
GREAT DANE
IF ONE WANTS SIZE COUPLED
WITH GOOD LOOKS
Pencil
12 x 8 inches
Illustrated: Page 88

93 (right)
IRISH WOLFHOUND
THIS HOUND IS EXCEPTIONALLY
GENTLE IN DISPOSITION
Inscribed with subtitle, 'Section
X' and '(Hounds)' on a detached
slip of paper
Pencil with chalk
6 ¾ x 8 inches
Illustrated: Page 119

94 GYPSY. A SCHNAUZER
Inscribed with title, 'Section XI' and 'Foreign & Fantastic Dogs'
on a detached slip of paper
Pencil, 9 ½ x 11 ¼ inches
Illustrated: Page 137

FELIKS TOPOLSKI

Feliks Topolski (1907-1989)

The significance of Feliks Topolski is suggested by those projects that were closest to his heart: the regular broadsheet, *Topolski's Chronicle* (1953-82), and the sequence of murals, *Memoir of the Century* (1975-89); for his drawings and paintings comprise a uniquely comprehensive yet impartial record of the age in which lived. He employed a swift, expressionist style for all of his projects, from illustrations to stage designs. This gave an emotional unity to his oeuvre, and even the smallest of his figures – such as a vignette for his edition of Bernard Shaw's *Pygmalion* (1941) – seems to speak volumes.

For a biography of Feliks Topolski, please refer to *The Illustrators*, 2011, pages 275-276.

The Rakes' Progress

The Rakes' Progress is a 1945 British film written and produced by Frank Launder and Sidney Gilliat, and directed by Sidney Gilliat. It has been described as 'part satiric critique, part ironic elegy' and 'one of the most fascinating films of the classical British cinema's richest period'. Feliks Topolski's 'atmospheric and somewhat lonely' drawings for the title sequence suggest that satire will not wholly dominate (Bruce Babington, *Launder and Gilliat: British Film Makers*, Manchester University Press, 2002, pages 94 & 98).

Based on a story by Val Valentine, who contributed to the screenplay, *The Rake's Progress* traces the decline of a modern upper-class playboy, Vivian Kenway, through a life of womanising, heavy drinking and running into debt, from being sent down from Oxford to causing the death of his father. Inspired in part by William Hogarth's series of paintings and engravings of the same name, the film departs from its source by allowing Kenway to redeem himself by dying in combat during the Second World War (as shown in the opening moments). Rex Harrison's sympathetic portrayal of Kenway is considered one of the best performances of his career.

95
ON THE EMBANKMENT
Pen ink and crayon
12 ¾ x 15 ¾ inches
Drawn for the title sequence of Sidney Gilliat and Frank Launder's film, *The Rake's Progress*, 1945, and also illustrated on the poster that advertises it

96 (opposite)
AT THE RACES
Pen and ink with crayon and pencil
12 ¾ x 15 ¾ inches
Drawn for the title sequence of Sidney Gilliat and Frank Launder's film, *The Rake's Progress*, 1945;
Similar to 'Derby', illustrated in Feliks Topolski, *Britain in Peace and War*, London: Methuen & Co, 1941

97
PASSPORT CONTROL
Pen ink and crayon with pencil
12 ¾ x 15 ¾ inches
Drawn for the title sequence of
Sidney Gilliat and Frank Launder's
film, *The Rake's Progress*, 1945

98
IN THE HOTEL LOBBY
Pen ink and crayon
12 ¾ x 15 ¾ inches
Drawn for the title sequence of
Sidney Gilliat and Frank Launder's
film, *The Rake's Progress*, 1945, and
also illustrated on the poster that
advertises it

GERARD HOFFNUNG

Gerard Hoffnung (1925-1959)

Gerard Hoffnung developed a unique vein of gentle, yet powerful humour, through drawings, lectures and even concerts – for his favourite subject was music at its most delightful and daft.

For a biography of Gerard Hoffnung, please refer to *The Illustrators*, 2011, page 257.

99
COMFORT READ
Signed
Inscribed 'not yearly, Tatler' below mount
Pen and ink with pencil
3 x 2 ½ inches
Provenance: Luke Gertler
Illustrated: *Tatler*

100
THE CAROL SINGERS
Signed
Watercolour and bodycolour with pencil
11 ½ x 8 ½ inches

ROWLAND EMETT
Frederick Rowland Emett, OBE (1906-1990)

Rowland Emett established himself as the creator of elegant and whimsical cartoons during the 1930s, while working as an industrial draughtsman. In 1951, he reached a wider public with his designs for The Far Tottering and Oyster Creek Railway, which was sited at Battersea Park during the Festival of Britain. Gradually, he converted more of his illustrations into increasingly complex three-dimensional machines. Both drawings and inventions helped cheer a nation fed up with years of austerity.

For a biography of Rowland Emett, please refer to *The Illustrators*, 2019, page 105.

The Mystery of the Merrifield

Thomas Adams's 'new Canadian novel', 'The Mystery of the Merrifield', was serialised in three parts between 21 May and 18 June 1960 in 'Canada's national magazine', *Maclean's*, which was then published fortnightly. A summary of the first part gives a flavour of the whole of this fantasy comedy adventure set during the Second World War:

> Chick McAllister, ignorant, ugly and craven, was washed overboard in an Atlantic storm. Another wave washed him back on board. When he regained consciousness he seemed briefly to have become a different man: witty, learned and dryly provoking. He had the crew of HMCS Merrifield in turmoil before he changed – at least for a time – into his old self.
> (*Maclean's*, 4 June 1960, page 22)

101
THE PIERHEAD REVELLERS
Signed
Pen ink and watercolour
on board
9 ¾ x 12 inches

102
REALITY – SEA AND
CORVETTE – FADED.
POTTER LOST HIMSELF IN
A CHIVALRIC REVERIE
STARRING ADMIRAL OF
THE FLEET LORD POTTER
Pen ink and watercolour
15 ½ x 22 inches
Illustrated: *Maclean's*, Toronto,
4 June 1960, Page 23,
'The Mystery of the Merrifield'
by Thomas Adams, Second of
Three Parts

103
AS THE SECONDS TICKED
BY, THE SOUND CHANGED
FROM A LONG-DRAWN-
OUT 'PIN-N-NG' TO A
SHARP 'PING-PONG'
Signed
Inscribed 'Classify contact as
follows: fish, whale, or
imagination ... Them Asdic guys
are so ping-happy – Part II'
below mount
Pen ink and watercolour
with bodycolour
10 ½ x 13 inches
Illustrated: *Maclean's*, Toronto,
4 June 1960, Page 50,
'The Mystery of the Merrifield'
by Thomas Adams, Second of
Three Parts

KATHLEEN HALE
Kathleen Hale, OBE (1898-2000)

Precocious and versatile, Kathleen Hale established herself as a member of the artistic circle of Fitzrovia while still in her twenties. However, it was marriage and motherhood that engendered her most immortal creation, Orlando the Marmalade Cat, and his adventures – which were first told to her sons as bedtime stories. The artwork and its reproduction for the first published stories set a new standard for children's illustrated books when they appeared in 1938.

For a biography of Kathleen Hale, please refer to *The Illustrators*, 2009, page 139.

104
ORLANDO IS DELIGHTED
WITH HIS WIDER MARGINS
Drawn on paper headed with
the artist's address
Inscribed with title
Watercolour with pencil
8 ¾ x 6 ½ inches

TOD HOUSE, FOREST HILL, Near OXFORD
STANTON ST. JOHN 390

Orlando the Marmalade Cat Goes to the Moon

106
ORLANDO'S LIST
Inscribed extensively with text
from the book below mount
Watercolour and pencil with
pen and ink
5 ½ x 6 ½ inches
Drawn for but not illustrated in
Kathleen Hale, *Orlando the
Marmalade Cat Goes to the Moon*,
London: John Murray, 1968

Reverse:
THE SAUCY CATSULE
Pen ink and watercolour with
pencil and bodycolour
3 ½ x 6 inches
Preliminary drawing for Kathleen
Hale, *Orlando the Marmalade Cat
Goes to the Moon*, London: John
Murray, 1968, Page 6

106 (reverse)

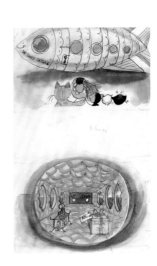

105
CHRISTMAS 1971
Signed
Watercolour with pencil
9 ¾ x 6 ¾ inches

107
SOME OF THE FLYING
SAUCERS WERE AS BIG AS
HOUSES, BUT ORLANDO
CAUGHT SMALL ONES IN
HIS NET AND CLIMBED
BACK WITH THEM INTO
THE SAUCY CATSULE
Watercolour with pen ink,
bodycolour and pencil
7 ½ x 6 inches
Preliminary drawings for
Kathleen Hale, *Orlando the
Marmalade Cat Goes to the Moon*,
London: John Murray, 1968,
Pages 14 and 13

Reverse:
SUDDENLY HE SAW HUNDREDS
OF FLYING SAUCERS FLASHING
PAST THE WINDOWS
Inscribed '... its castors to the
floor' and 'the cats landed'
below mount
Pen and ink
6 ¾ x 6 inches

108
THE SUMMER VISITORS
HAD ARRIVED, GREETING
EACH OTHER WITH
SHOUTS OF JOY. THE
LITTLE DOG LAUGHED TO
SEE SUCH FUN
Inscribed with title below mount
Pen ink and coloured inks
with watercolour, bodycolour
and pencil
7 ½ x 6 ½ inches
Preliminary drawing for Kathleen
Hale, *Orlando the Marmalade Cat
Goes to the Moon*, London:
John Murray, 1968, Page 26

FRED BANBERY
Frederick Ernest Banbery (1913-1999)

Fred Banbery made a strong impact as an illustrator on three
continents. Having become a staff artist for *The Times of India*
early in his career, he settled in the United States after the
Second World War, and contributed illustrations to a wide range
of books and periodicals. Working increasingly for British clients
from the mid 1950s, he made his most lasting contribution to our
illustrative tradition by determining the quintessential look of
Michael Bond's immortal character, Paddington Bear.

For a biography of Fred Banbery, please refer to *The Illustrators*, 2017,
page 198.

109
HE CLOSED HIS EYES, AND,
HOLDING HIS NOSE WITH
ONE PAW, HE JUMPED IN
Pen ink and watercolour with
bodycolour
6 x 5 ¾ inches
Provenance: The Estate of
Fred Banbery
Illustrated: Michael Bond,
Paddington Bear, London:
Collins, 1972, Page 26
Exhibited: 'Fred Banbery and
Paddington Bear', Chris Beetles
Gallery, April-May 2000

110
HE BEGAN MAKING
SOME MARMALADE
SANDWICHES
Pen ink and watercolour
5 ¾ x 5 ½ inches
Provenance: The Estate of
Fred Banberry
Illustrated: Michael Bond,
Paddington at the Tower,
London: Collins, 1975, Page 9
Exhibited: 'Fred Banbery and
Paddington Bear', Chris Beetles
Gallery, April-May 2000

8 Edward Ardizzone

EDWARD ARDIZZONE

Edward Ardizzone, CBE RA RDI (1900-1979)

Highly observant and immensely humane, the work of Edward Ardizzone is in direct descent from the finest French and English illustrators of the nineteenth century. Developing as an artist from 1930, Ardizzone made his name as an illustrator through his contributions to *The Radio Times* and then with *Little Tim and the Brave Sea Captain*, which proved to be one of the most significant picture books published between the wars. Soon considered one of the greatest illustrators of his generation, he also gained a reputation as an Official War Artist. Versatile and productive, he produced paintings, sculptures, etchings and lithographs, and worked as a designer.

For a biography of Edward Ardizzone, please refer to *The Illustrators*, 2019, page 79.

The Ceremony of Crossing the Line

The ceremony of crossing the line is an initiation rite that commemorates a person's crossing of the Equator. It has long been common in national and merchant navies, and is sometimes carried out for passengers' entertainment on civilian ocean liners and cruise ships. As in Edward Ardizzone's watercolour, the ceremony often involves sailors dressing as King Neptune, Queen Amphitrite and their entourage, who then preside over such proceedings as the shaving, bathing and beating of initiates. What should be fun can often get out of hand.

111
THE CEREMONY OF CROSSING THE LINE
Signed with initials
Inscribed with title on reverse
Watercolour sketch of 'King Neptune' on reverse
Watercolour with pencil
15 ¼ x 14 inches

Little Tim and Diana

The sale of Edward Ardizzone's original drawings to *Tim to the Rescue* (1949) and *Diana and her Rhinoceros* (1964) provides a rare opportunity to own a piece of the history of illustration. The artist's many skills came together in his own picture books, both those that comprise the 'Little Tim' series that confirmed his reputation and subsequent achievements. In Little Tim, he invented one of the most immortal characters of children's literature, essentially virtuous but with a thirst for adventure. However, Tim is almost matched in memorability by the sensitive and single-minded heroine of *Diana and her Rhinoceros*. And in the portrayal of children – their appearance, their posture, their movement – it is perhaps only E H Shepard who rivals the gentle genius of Ardizzone.

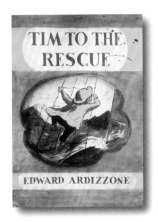

112
TIM TO THE RESCUE
Pen and ink female figure on reverse
Watercolour with pencil, and pen and ink on
translucent overlay
11 x 8 ¾ inches
Illustrated: Edward Ardizzone, *Tim to the Rescue*,
London: Oxford University Press, 1949,
Front Cover

Little Tim was in his house by the sea.

It was stormy weather and Tim, who was tired of his books

113
LITTLE TIM WAS IN HIS
HOUSE BY THE SEA
Watercolour and pencil with pen
and ink text, and pen and ink on
translucent overlay
9 x 7 inches
Illustrated: Edward Ardizzone,
Tim to the Rescue, London:
Oxford University Press, 1949,
[unpaginated]

and lessons was looking out of the window and was wishing that he was at sea again and having tremendous adventures on some ship tossing about among the waves.

But Tim had promised his parents to stay at home and work hard, and a promise like this has to be kept.

"Oh dear" said Tim to himself "I am bored with my sums, but I suppose I must learn them if I am to become a real grown up sailor."

Suddenly there was a knock at the door.

114
'OH DEAR' SAID TIM TO HIMSELF 'I AM BORED WITH MY SUMS, BUT I SUPPOSE I MUST LEARN THEM IF I AM TO BECOME A REAL GROWN UP SAILOR.'
Pen and ink
9 x 6 ¾ inches
Illustrated: Edward Ardizzone,
Tim to the Rescue, London:
Oxford University Press, 1949,
[unpaginated]

115
GINGER HAD HIS HAIR CUT,
BUT ALAS TO NO AVAIL
Watercolour with pencil and pen
and ink text, and pen and ink on
translucent overlay
9 x 13 inches
Illustrated: Edward Ardizzone, *Tim to the Rescue*, London:
Oxford University Press, 1949, [unpaginated]

Ginger became so unhappy that he took to hiding in the boats. His only friends were Tim and the ships cat, which says a lot for cats considering how nasty Ginger had been to it.

Tim would visit Ginger as often as he could and would bring him his dinner and cut his hair with a large pair of scissors that he had borrowed from seaman Bloggs.

116
TIM WOULD VISIT GINGER AS OFTEN AS HE COULD AND
WOULD BRING HIM HIS DINNER AND CUT HIS HAIR
Watercolour with pencil and pen and ink text, and pen and ink on
translucent overlay
8 ¾ x 14 inches
Illustrated: Edward Ardizzone, *Tim to the Rescue*, London:
Oxford University Press, 1949, [unpaginated]

Tim was standing on the bridge when he heard Captain Mc. Fee say to the mate "What do you think of the weather Mr. Mate? I don't like it a bit. There is a hurricane blowing up or I'll eat my hat. Order all hands on deck to batten down hatches and see that the ship's boys keep below."

117
EVEN THE SHIP'S CAT WAS
PUT OFF HIS DINNER
Pen and ink
9 x 6 ¾ inches
Illustrated: Edward Ardizzone,
Tim to the Rescue, London:
Oxford University Press, 1949,
[unpaginated]

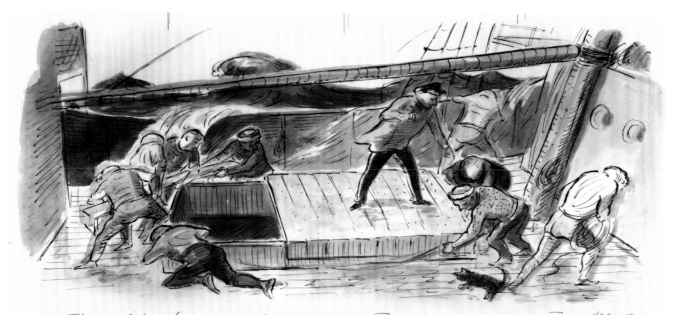

The next few hours were busy ones for the crew making everything ~~shipshape~~ secure *and shipshape on the decks.*

By now the wind was blowing great guns and the waves were getting bigger and bigger, occasionally dashing over the side and wetting the crew with spray.

But where was Ginger all the time? Still hiding in the boat. Tim had tried hard to make him come below, but he just would not.

118
THE NEXT FEW HOURS WERE BUSY ONES FOR THE
CREW MAKING EVERYTHING SECURE AND SHIPSHAPE ON
THE DECKS
Watercolour with pencil and pen and ink text, and pen and ink on
translucent overlay
9 × 14 inches
Illustrated: Edward Ardizzone, *Tim to the Rescue*, London:
Oxford University Press, 1949, [unpaginated]

would make him move, so Tim left
him to go back and get the crew to
help.   He had only gone a short way
on his dangerous homeward journey
when a tremendous wave rushed
down upon him.   He left for the
rigging and then looked round.

*Inside the boat was Ginger. He
was cold, wet and frightened and was
holding the ship's cat in his arms.
"Come below with me" shouted
Tim again and again; but the wild
wind only blew his words away.
At last Ginger heard. "No! No!"
he cried "I can't, I am too frightened".
Nothing that Tim could do or say*

*There was no boat,
no Ginger and no cat.*

119

INSIDE THE BOAT WAS GINGER. HE WAS COLD, WET
AND FRIGHTENED AND WAS HOLDING THE SHIP'S CAT
IN HIS ARMS
Pen and ink
9 x 13 ½ inches
Illustrated: Edward Ardizzone, *Tim to the Rescue*, London:
Oxford University Press, 1949, [unpaginated]

Captain Mc. Fee had seen them.
"All hands after to the rescue" he
shouted.
    Alaska Pete and Old Joe tied
themselves to ropes and with tre-
-mendous courage dashed across the
deck and soon had carried all
three of them back to safety.
    The Captain seemed furious. "How

dare you disobey my orders and be
on deck" he said to Tim and
Ginger.   "Go below below at once
and if I catch you on deck again
I will have you both beaten with a
ropes end."
    "Bosun" he roared   "Get that
boy's HAIR CUT."

120
ALASKA PETE AND OLD JOE SOON HAD CARRIED ALL THREE
OF THEM TO SAFETY
Pen and ink
9 x 13 ¼ inches
Illustrated: Edward Ardizzone, *Tim to the Rescue*, London:
Oxford University Press, 1949, [unpaginated]
A preliminary drawing for the right-hand drawing, 'How dare you disobey
my orders and be on deck', is underneath the published version.

Tim woke up feeling very well. He looked at Ginger and had a great surprise. Ginger's hair had not grown at all.

"Are you well Ginger" Tim said. "Yes fine" ans-wered Ginger.

"Well look at yourself in the glass" said Tim.

You can just imagine how pleased and surprised Ginger was to see his nice short hair.

Now, curious to tell, perhaps it was the cold sea water, perhaps it was the shock; but from Ginger this time on Ginger's hair grew in the ordinary slow way.

In a few days time the sun came out, the sea was calm, and the weather became warm and fine.

Tim and Ginger were back at their usual jobs, the crew were busy hanging out their clothes to dry, when the Captain ordered all hands to the "Forward" Well deck. There he made a speech from the bridge.

"Men" he said "during the storm the two ship's boys disobeyed my orders and nearly got drowned.

However, now that I have heard the full story I realise that ship's boy

121
YOU CAN IMAGINE HOW PLEASED AND SURPRISED GINGER
WAS TO SEE HIS NICE SHORT HAIR
Pen and ink
9 x 13 ¾ inches
Illustrated: Edward Ardizzone, *Tim to the Rescue*, London:
Oxford University Press, 1949, [unpaginated]

But — Tim's proudest moment came when there arrived by post a beautiful gold medal and a roll of parchment on which was written the story of his brave adventure.

Tim's father had the roll framed and hung it in the drawing room.

122
TIM'S PROUDEST MOMENT CAME
WHEN THERE ARRIVED BY POST
A BEAUTIFUL GOLD MEDAL AND
A ROLL OF PARCHMENT ON
WHICH WAS WRITTEN THE
STORY OF HIS BRAVE ADVENTURE
Pen and ink
9 x 6 ¾ inches
Illustrated: Edward Ardizzone,
Tim to the Rescue, London:
Oxford University Press, 1949,
[unpaginated]

— THE END —

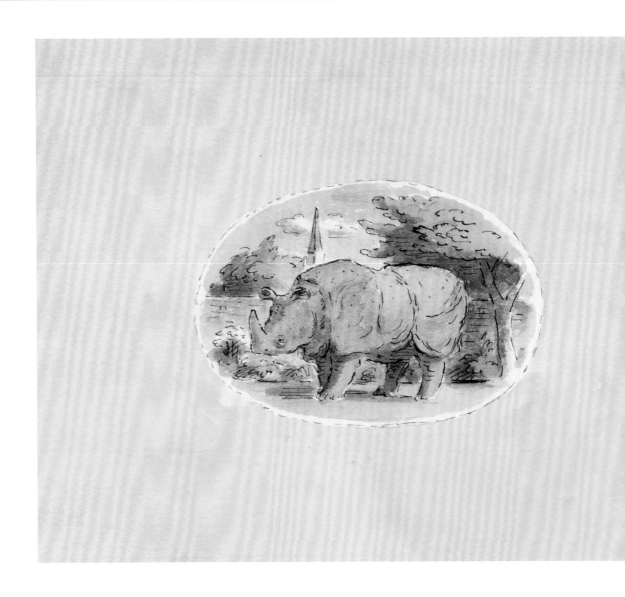

123
DIANA AND HER RHINOCEROS
Pen ink and watercolour
8 ¼ x 21 ½ inches
Illustrated: Edward Ardizzone, *Diana and her Rhinoceros*, London:
The Bodley Head, 1964, Cover

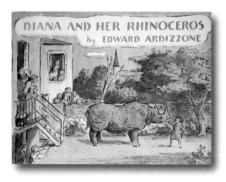

124
DIANA WAS SITTING IN FRONT OF THE FIRE MAKING HOT
BUTTERED TOAST, WHICH WAS MR EFFINGHAM-JONES'S
FAVOURITE FOOD
Pen and ink
5 x 7 ½ inches
Illustrated: Edward Ardizzone, *Diana and her Rhinoceros*, London:
The Bodley Head, 1964, Page 4

125
INTO THE ROOM CAME THE HEAD OF AN ENORMOUS
RHINOCEROS WITH THE BABY'S JACKET ROUND ITS HORN
Pen ink and watercolour
5 x 7 ½ inches
Illustrated: Edward Ardizzone, *Diana and her Rhinoceros*, London:
The Bodley Head, 1964, Page 6

126
MRS EFFINGHAM-JONES CRIED, 'OOEE! OOEE! IT'S EATEN THE
BABY', AND FELL ON THE FLOOR IN A DEADLY FAINT
Pen ink and watercolour
4 ¼ x 7 ¾ inches
Illustrated: Edward Ardizzone, *Diana and her Rhinoceros*, London:
The Bodley Head, 1964, Page 7

127
DIANA WENT ON POURING ALL THESE MEDICINES DOWN
THE RHINOCEROS'S THROAT
Pen ink and watercolour
4 ¼ x 8 inches
Illustrated: Edward Ardizzone, *Diana and her Rhinoceros*, London:
The Bodley Head, 1964, Page 10

128
THE DOOR OPENED AND THERE STOOD THREE MEN WITH GUNS
Pen ink and watercolour with typed text, including title, on collaged paper, on two
joined sheets of paper
5 ½ x 16 inches
Illustrated: Edward Ardizzone, *Diana and her Rhinoceros*, London:
The Bodley Head, 1964, Pages 14-15

129
THE ONLY TROUBLE WAS THAT THE RHINOCEROS WAS VERY
FOND OF EATING DAHLIAS
Pen ink and watercolour
4 ½ x 8 ¼ inches
Illustrated: Edward Ardizzone, *Diana and her Rhinoceros*, London:
The Bodley Head, 1964, Page 19

130

GROWN-UPS NEVER CEASED TO WONDER AT ITS TAMENESS,
WHILE CHILDREN LOVED TO PLAY WITH IT
Pen ink and watercolour on two joined sheets of paper
5 x 17 inches
Illustrated: Edward Ardizzone, *Diana and her Rhinoceros*,
London: The Bodley Head, 1964, Pages 22-23

131
DIANA FED HIM WITH SO MUCH HOT BUTTERED TOAST
THAT HE WAS GETTING JUST A LITTLE TOO FAT
Pen ink and watercolour
3 ½ x 7 inches
Illustrated: Edward Ardizzone, *Diana and her Rhinoceros*, London:
The Bodley Head, 1964, Page 26

132

IT WAS A RATHER GREEDY OLD BEAST AND IF DIANA DID
NOT GIVE IT THE TOAST FAST ENOUGH IT MADE A NOISE
WHICH SOUNDED LIKE 'HURRYUPWITHTHETOAST'
Pen and ink
4 ½ x 8 inches
Illustrated: Edward Ardizzone, *Diana and her Rhinoceros*, London:
The Bodley Head, 1964, Page 28

133
DIANA AND HER RHINOCEROS ARE WITH US STILL
Pen and ink
5 × 6 inches
Illustrated: Edward Ardizzone, *Diana and her Rhinoceros*, London: The Bodley Head, 1964, Page 32

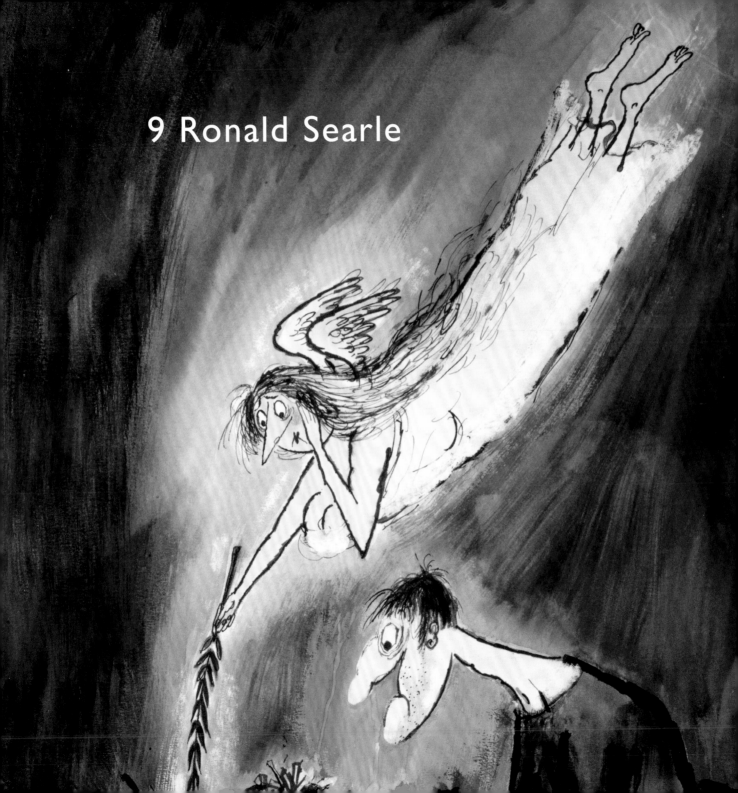

RONALD SEARLE
Ronald William Fordham Searle, CBE (1920-2011)

Equally inspired by a wide range of experience and a great knowledge of the history of caricature, Ronald Searle honed an incisive graphic skill to develop an unparalleled graphic oeuvre, an oeuvre that has made him one of the most popular and influential cartoonist-illustrators.

For a biography of Ronald Searle, please refer to *The Illustrators*, 2018, page 94.

For essays on various aspects of Ronald Searle's achievement, see *The Illustrators*, 1999, pages 228-230; and *The Illustrators*, 2000, pages 40-42.

Chris Beetles Ltd publishes Russell Davies's *Ronald Searle*. In the 2003 edition of the 1990 biography, Russell Davies and Ronald Searle have added corrections and brought up to date the exhibitions list and bibliography.

Chris Beetles Gallery also held the major tribute exhibition, 'Ronald Searle Remembered', in May-June 2012. It was accompanied by a 200 page fully illustrated paperback catalogue, containing newly researched essays and notes.

The Increasing Fame of St Trinian's

Originally appearing in *Lilliput* from 1941, Ronald Searle's cartoons about St Trinian's girls' school were gathered by Macdonald & Co in mixed collections of cartoons, beginning with *Hurrah for St Trinian's! and Other Lapses* (1948). Though Searle began to tire of his creation by 1951, a year later he allowed his *News Chronicle* colleague, 'Timothy Shy' (D B Wyndham Lewis), to write a narrative about the school, and illustrated the resulting comic romance, *The Terror of St Trinian's*. The great success of this *jeu d'esprit* – published by Max Parrish – was fuelled by a publicity stunt in which a group of young women, dressed as schoolgirls, invaded Foyle's bookshop. From that point, Searle attempted to bring his involvement with St Trinian's to an end, even publishing *Souls in Torment* (1953) as 'a funeral rite' (Russell Davies, Page 101). However, once Frank Launder and Sidney Gilliat were allowed to produce a film inspired by Searle's drawings, in 1954, St Trinian's developed a life of its own, making it impossible to quash. Starring George Cole, Joyce Grenfell and Alastair Sim, *The Belles of St Trinian's* immediately entered the popular imagination and, for many people, remains the point of entry to exploring the best-known girls' school in the world. Furthermore, Searle was directly involved in the film and its three most immediate sequels, providing drawings for their title sequences and designing posters to advertise them.

134
ANYONE FOR KARATE?
Signed, inscribed with title and dated 1952
Pen and ink
6 x 9 inches
Illustrated: Ronald Searle, *The Terror of St Trinian's*, London: Max Parrish, 1952, Page 48; Ronald Searle, *The St Trinian's Story*, London: Perpetua Books, 1959, Page 66

'Anyone for Karate?'

135
SAME OLD STUFF …
Signed
Inscribed with title on supporting sheet
Pen and ink
7 ¼ x 4 ¾ inches
Illustrated: *Lilliput*, 1946;
Ronald Searle, *The Female Approach*,
New York: Knopf, 1954, Page 47;
Ronald Searle, *St Trinian's: The Entire
Appalling Business*, New York: Rookery
Press, 2008

136

PREPARING TO BE A
BEAUTIFUL LADY?
Signed and inscribed with title
and 'Lilliput March 1947 issue'
and 'St Trinian's No 8. Hurrah
for St Trinian's 1948 (Page 56)'
Pen and ink with pencil
10 ¼ x 6 ½ inches
Illustrated: *Lilliput*, March 1947;
Ronald Searle, *Hurrah for
St Trinian's*, London: Macdonald's,
1948, Page 56

137
CAVE!
Signed and inscribed with title
and 'Lilliput Jan 47' and 'Hurrah
page 57 1948'
Pen and ink with bodycolour
and pencil
10 ¼ x 7 ¼ inches
Illustrated: *Lilliput*, January 1947;
Ronald Searle, *Hurrah for
St Trinian's*, London: Macdonald,
1948, Page 57

The Punch Revue

The Punch Revue opened at the Duke of York's Theatre, in St Martin's Lane, London, on 28 September 1955. Instigated by *Punch*'s radical new editor, Malcolm Muggeridge, it was devised and directed by Vida Hope, with a book written by Ronald Duncan. Other contributors included W H Auden, John Betjeman, T S Eliot and Louis MacNeice, and the composers, Larry Adler, Benjamin Britten and Donald Swann. Two of Eliot's poems from *Old Possum's Book of Practical Cats* were dramatised and performed a quarter of a century before Andrew Lloyd Webber created *Cats*. However, the revue was badly received – being booed on the first night and considered to lack the bite of the magazine – and it closed after a short run.

138
THE PUNCH REVUE
Signed
Pen ink, watercolour and bodycolour
19 ¾ x 13 inches
Design for poster and programme cover for *The Punch Revue*, which opened at the Duke of York's Theatre, London, on 28 September 1955

139
IF MUSIC BE THE FOOD OF LOVE ...
Signed and dated 1956
Inscribed with title and publishing details, and dated 1956 on reverse
Pen ink and watercolour
11 x 12 ½ inches
Illustrated: *Punch*, 14 March 1956, Page 314;
Ronald Searle, *Merry England Etc,* London: Perpetua Books, 1957, Page 100

HOLIDAY How to take advantage
of Italian Men.

140
HOW TO TAKE ADVANTAGE OF
ITALIAN MEN
Inscribed with title and 'Holiday'
Pen and ink
15 ½ x 10 ¾ inches
Illustrated: *Holiday*, New York

141
THE ANGEL OF INSPIRATION
Signed
Pen ink and watercolour
with bodycolour
17 ¼ x 12 ¾ inches

Rehearsals at the 'Lido', Paris, 1961
The Parisian cabaret theatre known as Le Lido opened at 78 Avenue des
Champs-Elysées in 1946 (and moved to its current location at No 116 in
1977). Its performances always include the famous Bluebell Girls, who can
be seen rehearsing the show, *Pour Vous*, at the centre of Ronald Searle's
image. Stars who have appeared at Le Lido include Maurice Chevalier,
Laurel & Hardy, Noël Coward, Marlene Dietrich, Josephine Baker,
Edith Piaf, Shirley MacLaine and Elton John.

142
REHEARSALS AT THE 'LIDO', PARIS, 1961
Signed and dated 'Lido Dec 1961'
Inscribed 'Rehearsals at the "Lido"', publication details and dimensions in
centimetres, and dated '4 Dec 1961' on reverse of supporting board
Pen ink and watercolour on board
16 ½ x 22 ½ inches
Illustrated: *Le Nouveau Candide*, Paris, 7 December 1961

143
WHO KILLED HOLLYWOOD SOCIETY?
Signed and inscribed with title
Pen ink and watercolour
11 x 14 inches
Illustrated: *TV Guide*, New York, 11 November 1967, Page 27,
'Who Killed Hollywood Society? 3 The Golden Years' by Cleveland Amory

'He looked frightful — an unsanitary fur-ball the size of an Alsatian, with a garnish of
twigs and leaves entwined in his knotted coat, bones protruding from his body and an
immense brown nose poking through the undergrowth of his moustache.'

(Peter Mayle, *Toujours Provence*, London: Hamish Hamilton, 1991)

144
THE DOG 'BOY'
Signed, inscribed with title,
story title and 'P Mayle', and dated 1991
Pen ink and watercolour with pencil
15 ¾ x 21 ¼ inches
Illustrated: *Telegraph Magazine*, 13 April
1991, 'Toujours Provence: The Lost Dog'
by Peter Mayle

NORMAN THELWELL
Norman Thelwell (1923-2004)

Norman Thelwell is arguably the most popular cartoonist to have worked in Britain since the Second World War. Though almost synonymous with his immortal subject of little girls and their fat ponies, his work is far more wide ranging, perceptive – and indeed prescient – than that association suggests.

Norman Thelwell was born in Tranmere, Birkenhead, Cheshire on 3 May 1923, the younger son of a maintenance engineer at Lever Brothers, Port Sunlight. He was educated locally at Well Lane Primary School and Rock Ferry High School, where he began to show a talent for drawing.

In 1939, Thelwell joined a Liverpool dock office as a junior clerk and, on the outbreak of war, spent nights fire watching. Three years later, he joined the second battalion of the East Yorkshire Regiment, and was soon transferred to the intelligence section because of his ability to draw. During training as a wireless operator in 1944, he took some evening classes at Nottingham School of Art. Later that year, he was posted to India with the Royal Electrical and Mechanical Engineers, subsequently becoming Art Editor and sole artist for a new army magazine published in New Delhi. While in that position, he had his first cartoon published in *London Opinion* and a weekly series of caricatures of India service leaders published in *News Review*.

After the war, Thelwell studied at Liverpool City School of Art (1947-50) and lectured on design and illustration at Wolverhampton College of Art (1950-56). He sold his first drawing to *Punch* in 1950, and two years later became an important regular contributor. He also worked as a cartoonist for several newspapers (the *News Chronicle*, the *Sunday Dispatch* and the *Sunday Express*) and began to produce his own comic books (beginning with *Angels on Horseback*, 1957). Many of these books centre upon country life and county pursuits, and their light-hearted images are founded upon a thorough knowledge of their topics; Thelwell was, for instance, both a fine landscape watercolourist and an enthusiastic angler. However, he surveyed an impressive range of aspects of British life, so providing the public with a constantly entertaining visual indicator of social change.

From 1959, Thelwell and his family lived in Hampshire, first in Braishfield, near Romsey, and then, from 1968, in Timsbury. He also restored a mill near Callington, Cornwall, recounting the experience in *A Millstone Round My Neck* (1981). He died in Winchester on 7 February 2004.

Further reading
Mark Bryant, 'Thelwell, Norman (1923-2004)', H C G Matthew and Brian Harrison (eds), *Oxford Dictionary of National Biography*, Oxford University Press, 2008, https://doi.org/10.1093/ref:odnb/93356

Having mounted major exhibitions of the work of Thelwell in 1989 and 1991, Chris Beetles encouraged further interest in the artist with 'The Definitive Thelwell' in 2009, and its accompanying catalogue. The 100 page, colour catalogue surveys all aspects of his career, through 177 illustrations, an appreciation, a biographical chronology and a full bibliography.

145
SHOOTING PARTY
Signed
Pen and ink
8 ½ x 10 ¾ inches

146
I THINK WE'VE GOT
A STOWAWAY
Signed and inscribed with title
Pen and ink
7 ¼ x 10 ¼ inches
Provenance: The Artist's Estate

"I THINK WE'VE GOT A STOWAWAY"

147
MAY WE BORROW A CUP
OF ENGINE OIL?
Signed and inscribed with title
Pen and ink
6 ¾ x 10 inches
Provenance: The Artist's Estate

"MAY WE BORROW A CUP OF ENGINE OIL?"

148
MAKE SURE YOU HAVE
SOME SUITABLE
ENTERTAINMENT
ARRANGED FOR A
WET DAY
Signed and inscribed with title
Pen and ink with bodycolour
6 ¼ x 9 ¾ inches
Provenance: The Artist's Estate

149
IF THESE ANTARCTIC
HOLIDAY TOURS CATCH
ON, THIS PLACE IS GOING
TO LOOK LIKE
BLACKPOOL BEACH IN A
FEW YEARS TIME
Signed and inscribed with title
Pen ink and watercolour
7 ¾ x 10 ¼ inches
Illustrated: *Punch*, 31 July 1968,
Page 160

150
RODEO
Signed
Pen ink and watercolour
7 ¼ x 9 ¾ inches
Illustrated: Design for colour print, 1973

151
THE FIRST FENCE
Signed with initial
Pen and ink
5 x 7 ½ inches
Provenance: The Artist's Estate

152
SQUEEZING THROUGH
Signed
Pen and ink
7 x 8 ¼ inches
Provenance: The Artist's Estate

153
THE SHOW CHAMPION
Signed with initial
Inscribed with title below mount
Pen and ink
5 ¾ x 7 inches
Provenance: The Artist's Estate

154
I PREFERRED THE NAME,
'MERRYLEGS'
Signed and inscribed with title
Pen and ink
6 ¾ x 8 ¾ inches
Provenance: The Artist's Estate

155
FREE RANGE CHRISTMAS POULTRY
Signed
Pen ink and pencil
7 x 9 ½ inches
Provenance: The Artist's Estate

11 John Glashan

JOHN GLASHAN

John Glashan (1927-1999)

John Glashan was best known as the creator of the cartoon strip, 'Genius', which developed a cult following during its five-year run in the *Observer*. His passion for fine watercolour painting allowed him to develop his world of tiny figures inhabiting beautiful, vast, baroque interiors and sweeping landscapes.

For a biography of John Glashan, please refer to *The Illustrators*, 2017, Page 216.

156
THE MAN WHO INVENTED THE PIZZA CONDUCTING HIS OWN DEFENCE AT THE OLD BAILEY
CHIEF CHARACTER WITNESS: THE MAN WHO INVENTED THE PHILLIPS SCREW
Signed
Watercolour with pen ink and bodycolour
14 ½ x 21 inches
Provenance: The Artist's Estate
Illustrated: *The Spectator*, 9 March 1991

The man who invented the Pizza conducting his own defence at the Old Bailey.

Chief character witness: the man who invented the Phillips screw.

157
DON'T
Signed
Watercolour with pen and ink
17 ¾ x 24 inches
Provenance: The Artist's Estate
Illustrated: *The Spectator*, 27 April 1991

158
WRITER LOOKING FOR PEOPLE
TO PUT INTO HIS
EIGHTY-SEVENTH NOVEL
Signed
Watercolour with pen and ink
11 x 14 ½ inches
Provenance: The Artist's Estate
Illustrated: *The Spectator*, 1 February 1992

159
REGRET, SENOR, LAST
CIGARETTE EES NON
PERMISSABLE, AS SMOKING CAN
CAUSE FATAL DISEASES
Signed
Watercolour with pen ink and bodycolour
11 x 15 inches
Provenance: The Artist's Estate
Illustrated: *The Spectator*, 20 February 1993

160
YOU COME FROM A BETTER BROKEN HOME THAN I DO
Signed
Watercolour with pen ink and bodycolour
14 x 20 ¾ inches
Provenance: The Artist's Estate
Illustrated: *The Spectator*, 6 February 1993

Supposing we appealed to the electorate to commit mass suicide.

Do you think they'd stand for it?

They might just, if we offered them free baseball caps.

John Glashan

161
'SUPPOSING WE APPEALED TO THE ELECTORATE TO
COMMIT MASS SUICIDE.'
'DO YOU THINK THEY'D STAND FOR IT?'
'THEY MIGHT JUST, IF WE OFFERED THEM FREE BASEBALL CAPS.'
Signed
Watercolour with pen ink and bodycolour
11 x 14 ½ inches
Provenance: The Artist's Estate
Illustrated: *The Spectator*, 28 November 1992

162
PERHAPS YOU WOULD PREFER THIS ROOM, MISTER HARRINGTON,
IT DOESN'T HAVE THE OPPRESSIVE WOOD CARVINGS
Signed
Watercolour with pen ink and bodycolour
15 x 21 ¾ inches
Provenance: The Artist's Estate
Illustrated: *The Spectator*, 4 December 1993

163
'DON'T YOU EVER SMILE?'
'I DID ONCE, ABOUT TEN YEARS AGO,
AND IT GAVE ME A HEADACHE.'
Signed
Watercolour with pen and ink
14 x 20 ¼ inches
Provenance: The Artist's Estate
Illustrated: *The Spectator*, 15 January 1994

I've still got a headache.

164
I'VE STILL GOT A HEADACHE
Signed
Watercolour with pen ink and bodycolour
14 x 21 ½ inches
Provenance: The Artist's Estate
Illustrated: *The Spectator*, 15 October 1994

165
'HOW DO YOU MANAGE TO LOOK TWENTY-EIGHT ALL THE TIME?'
'I'M SEVENTEEN.'
Signed
Watercolour with pen ink and bodycolour
10 ½ x 14 inches
Provenance: The Artist's Estate
Illustrated: *The Spectator*, 26 November 1994

12 Mark
Boxer

TATLER

MARC (MARK BOXER)
Charles Mark Edward Boxer (1931-1988),
known as 'Marc' and 'Mark Boxer'

As one of the greatest caricaturists of the twentieth century, Mark Boxer satirised the country's social elite – a world of beautiful, fashionable, metropolitan figures of which he himself was very much a part. Equally adept as a social cartoonist, he effectively captured the lives of the upper-middle classes, continuing this great tradition from the likes of Pont and Osbert Lancaster.

For a biography of Mark Boxer, please refer to *The Illustrators*, 2017, page 226.

Lord Lichfield

Patrick Anson (1939-2005), known professionally as Patrick Lichfield, became 5th Earl Lichfield in 1960. His role as official photographer at the wedding of the Prince and Princess of Wales in 1981 increased his standing as one of Britain's best-known photographers, particularly of portraits of performers and society figures. Exhibitions of his work include a retrospective held at the Chris Beetles Gallery in 2007. He and Mark Boxer had worked together during the 1960s on Jocelyn Stevens's society magazine, *Queen*.

The Ex-Foreign Secretary Bird. Selwyn Lloyd

The Conservative politician, John Selwyn Lloyd (1904-1978), was best known as the Foreign Secretary (1955-60), under Anthony Eden, during the Suez Crisis, and then under Harold Macmillan. He proved less successful as Chancellor of the Exchequer (1960-62), and was sacked by Macmillan during the famous cabinet reshuffle known as the 'Night of the Long Knives'. However, he returned to office under Alec Douglas-Home as Leader and Shadow Leader of the House of Commons (1963-65), and ended his parliamentary career as Speaker of the House of Commons (1971-76). Mark Boxer shows him in this last role.

166
LORD LICHFIELD
Signed
Pen and ink
13 x 8 ½ inches

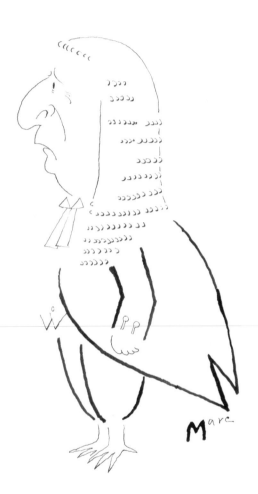

167 (above)
THE EX-FOREIGN
SECRETARY BIRD
SELWYN LLOYD
Signed and inscribed with title
Pen and ink
9 ½ x 4 ½ inches

168 (above right)
MALCOLM MUGGERIDGE
Signed and inscribed with title
Pen and ink
9 ½ x 7 ½ inches

Malcolm Muggeridge

Always critical of contemporary society, the journalist and satirist, Malcolm Muggeridge (1903-1990), moved from an independent socialist point of view to a right-wing religious one. He was deputy editor of the *Daily Telegraph* (1950-52) and a controversial editor of *Punch* (1953-57). Following the notorious article, 'Does England Really Need a Queen?', published in the American magazine, *The Saturday Evening Post*, in 1957, he moved into broadcasting, appearing regularly on BBC television's *Panorama* and producing religious documentaries, including *Something Beautiful for God* (1969), about Mother Teresa of Calcutta. As result of her influence, he converted to Roman Catholicism in 1982. This is referenced in Mark Boxer's drawing by the rosary that Muggeridge fingers.

OWN GOAL

Ally MacLeod

The Scottish footballer and manager, Alistair 'Ally' MacLeod
(1931-2004), is best known as the manager of Scotland's
national team during the years 1977-78, and especially during
its appearance at the 1978 FIFA World Cup, held in Argentina.
During that tournament, the team scored a 3-2 victory against
the Netherlands, but was still eliminated on goal difference.
Though MacLeod resigned soon after, he stated in his 1979
autobiography, that 'I am a very good manager who just
happened to have a few disastrous days, once upon a time,
in Argentina'. Beginning his professional career with Third
Lanarck in 1949, he played for four other Scottish League
teams, including Ayr United, which he subsequently managed.
He would go on to manage four further Scottish League teams.

169
ALLY MACLEOD
Signed
Pen and ink
12 ½ x 6 ½ inches

Jonathan Meades

Jonathan Meades (born 1947) is a wide-ranging writer and film-maker, who has shown particular passions for architecture and food. His positions have included television critic for the *Observer* (1977-79), features editor for *Tatler* (1982-86, at the time that Mark Boxer was Editor-in-Chief) and restaurant critic for *The Times* (1986-2000), winning Best Food Journalist at the Glenfiddich Awards on four occasions. He has published fiction as well as non-fiction, including two novels. His idiosyncratic work in television began in 1985, and has included the series, *The Victorian House* (Channel 4, 1987), *Abroad in Britain* (BBC2, 1990, and its sequels), *Meades Eats* (BBC4, 2003), *Jonathan Meades: Off Kilter* (BBC4, 2009) and *Jonathan Meades in France* (BBC4, 2012), as well as a number of individual television films. Having trained at RADA, he prefers to be considered a performer rather than a presenter.

170
JONATHAN MEADES
Signed
Pen and ink with pencil and bodycolour
11 x 8 ¼ inches

John Gross keeping up with the jeunesse d'oré

John Gross Keeping Up with the Jeunesse d'oré

The son of East European Jewish immigrants, John Gross (1935-2011) graduated from Oxford and Princeton, and rose to become a fellow of King's College, Cambridge, editor of *The Times Literary Supplement* (1974-81), senior book editor of *The New York Times* (1983-89) and theatre critic of the *Daily Telegraph* (1989-2005). His works as an author include *The Rise and Fall of the Man of Letters* (which won the Duff Cooper Prize for 1969), while *The New Oxford Book of English Prose* (1998) is among the best-loved of his anthologies. Though known for his modesty, he was much praised by colleagues and others, and described in obituaries as 'the best-read man in Britain'. The title of Mark Boxer's portrait – which illustrated some of those obituaries – hints at the breadth of his knowledge and acquaintance.

171
JOHN GROSS KEEPING UP WITH THE JEUNESSE D'ORE
Signed and inscribed with title
Pen and ink
11 ½ x 8 ¼ inches
Illustrated: *The Spectator*, 15 January 2011, 'The man who read everything: John Gross (1935-2011)' by Craig Brown;
Wall Street Journal, 15 January 2011, 'A Tonic, Humane and Civilising Force' [obituary of John Gross], by Roger Kimball

172
PUT ON YOUR WELLINGTONS, SIMON,
AND WE'LL TRY THAT BISTRO IN CHELSEA ...
Signed
Pen and ink
7 x 3 ¾ inches
Illustrated: *The Times*

173
WE HAD A REALLY OLD-FASHIONED EASTER. WE
WENT ON A CND MARCH AND THE KIDS WERE
ARRESTED AT MARGATE
Signed
Pen and ink, 7 ½ x 3 ¾ inches
Illustrated: *The Times*

174
IT'S SIMPLE – I WEAR MY WHITE POPPY IN
HAMPSTEAD AND MY RED ONE IN THE COUNTRY
Signed
Pen and ink
7 x 3 ¾ inches
Illustrated: *The Times*

175
AND ON THE PACK WHAT ABOUT
'IF YOU SMOKE THESE YOU MAY NOT
LIVE TO BE A GERIATRIC'
Signed
Pen and ink, 7 ¼ x 3 ¾ inches
Illustrated: *The Times*, 7 January 1971

13 The Americans

WILLIAM STEIG

William Steig (1907-2003)

One of the most famous and talented illustrators and cartoonists that America has ever produced, William Steig worked in a remarkable array of styles across a career that spanned over 70 years. His work is instantly recognisable despite frequent adaption and experimentation, from his classic one liner cartoons and cover artwork from the golden age of *The New Yorker* – that stand alongside the likes of Charles Addams and Peter Arno – to Picassoesque portraits and geometric creations that rival Saul Steinberg. In later life he reinvented himself as an illustrator of books for children, to huge success, creating immortal characters such as Shrek, the inspiration for the Academy Award-winning film.

William Steig was born in Brooklyn, New York, on 14 November 1907, the third of four sons of Joseph Steig, a house painter, and his wife, Laura Ebel Steig, a seamstress, Jewish immigrants from Lviv, in what is now Ukraine. Joseph Steig had arrived in New York in 1903 and was joined shortly after by his wife and first son, Irwin. William Steig was the second son born in Brooklyn, after his brother Henry, before the family then moved to the Bronx, where the youngest son, Arthur, was born. Steig's parents were also artists, who encouraged Steig and his brothers to follow this passion. Steig drew his first cartoons for his high school newspaper, and graduated in 1923 at the age of 15. He studied for two years at City College in New York, and for three years at the National Academy of Design, before being accepted into Yale, though he dropped out after just five days.

Steig's first cartoon appeared in *The New Yorker* in 1930, the start of an association that would last for 73 years. During that period, he produced over 1,600 cartoons for the magazine and over 120 covers. In addition to his work for *The New Yorker*, he also began contributing to such magazines as *Judge, Life, Vanity Fair* and *Collier's*. Many of his early cartoons in *The New Yorker* depicted tough, streetwise kids, inspired by his childhood on the streets of the Bronx. These kids became known as Steig's 'Small Fry', and inspired the first collection of his cartoons, published under that title in 1944. Though he produced many one-liner cartoons in the classic *New Yorker* style, his work appeared in a great variety of styles, from portraits inspired by his artistic idol, Pablo Picasso, to geometric figure studies.

In 1936, Steig began producing cartoons in another very particular style, making what he referred to as 'symbolic drawings'. These line drawings personified emotional troubles and states of mind, from shame and depression, to embarrassment and nausea, and even to less defined characters such as 'public opinion no longer worries me' and 'pleasant chap but never a friend'. He showed these drawings to *The New Yorker* editor Harold Ross, who believed that, though one day they would be hailed as genius, they were not right for the magazine, being 'too personal and not funny enough'. Steig's 'symbolic drawings' were later published in the collections *About People* (1939), *The Lonely Ones* (1942) and *All Embarrassed* (1944) to critical acclaim.

In the year that Steig began creating his 'symbolic drawings', he married his first wife, Elizabeth Mead, sister of the anthropologist, Margaret Mead. Their divorce ten years later led Steig to seek the help of the psychiatrist, Wilhelm Reich (1897-1957), a disciple of Sigmund Freud. Though considered controversial due to his belief in a cosmic energy known as orgones, Reich would become a psychological mentor for Steig, who would illustrate Reich's manifesto, *Listen, Little Man!* in 1948, and dedicate his book *The Agony in the Kindergarten* (1950) to him. In 1950, Steig married Kari Homestead, and the following year published a series of drawings of jilted men and cold women in *The Rejected Lovers*. They divorced in 1963 and the following year he married Stephanie Healey. This marriage lasted just two years, before he married Jeanne Doron in 1968. They would stay married for the rest of his life.

In 1967, a fellow cartoonist at *The New Yorker*, Bob Kraus, founded the publishing company Windmill Books, and convinced Steig to try writing a book for children. The following year, at the age of 61, he published his first children's books, *CDB!* and *Roland the Minstrel Pig*. Over the next 35 years, he published over 40 books for children, such as *Dominic* (1972), *Abel's Island* (1976), *The Amazing Bone* (1976), *Rotten Island* (1984), *Spinky Sulks* (1988) and *Zeke Pippin* (1994). He won the Caldecott Medal, awarded for the most distinguished American picture book for children, for *Sylvester and the Magic Pebble* in 1969, and the John Newbery Medal for the most distinguished contribution to American literature for children for *Doctor De Soto* in 1982. Perhaps Steig's most famous creation was *Shrek!* (1990), which inspired the Academy Award-winning feature film *Shrek* (2001) and its sequels.

Though he grew up a New Yorker, he spent much of his life living in Kent, Connecticut. In 1992, he moved to Boston, Massachusetts, where he died on 3 October 2003, aged 95. He was survived by his wife, two children from his first marriage, a daughter from his second marriage, and two grandchildren.

From November 2007 to March 2008, the Jewish Museum in New York held the retrospective exhibition 'From *The New Yorker* to Shrek: The Art of William Steig'. The exhibition travelled to the Contemporary Jewish Museum in San Francisco, California from June to September 2009.

The work of William Steig is represented in the collections of the Art Institute of Chicago, the Brooklyn Museum, the Eric Carle Museum of Picturebook Art, Amherst MA and the Norman Rockwell Museum, Stockbridge MA.

The biography of William Steig is written by Alexander Beetles.

Further reading on William Steig

Claudia J Nahson, *The Art of William Steig*, The Jewish Museum, New York/New Haven: Yale University Press, 2007;

Denis Wepman, 'Steig, William (14 Nov 1907-3 Oct 2003)', John A Garratty & Mark C Carnes (eds), *American National Biography*, New York: Oxford University Press, 2018, https://doi.org/10.1093/anb/9780198606697.013.1702003

Til Death Do Us Part

Nos **176-183** are all illustrated in William Steig, *Til Death Do Us Part: some ballet notes on marriage*, New York: Duell, Sloan and Pearce, 1947, [unpaginated]

176

THE HAPPY COUPLE

Signed

Pen and ink

5 ¾ x 4 ¼ inches

Illustrated: Front Cover

Literature: *The New York Times*, 23 February 1947

'Marriage – by Wm Steig' by Charles Poore

177

HE'S MINE – ALL MINE

Signed

Inscribed with title below mount

Pen and ink

5 ½ x 5 inches

Literature: *The New York Times*, 23 February 1947, 'Marriage – by Wm Steig' by Charles Poore

178

YOU'RE SO CUTE I COULD EAT YOU
Signed
Inscribed with title below mount
Pen and ink
5 ¼ x 4 ½ inches

179

OUR MARRIAGE WILL BE DIFFERENT
Signed
Inscribed with title below mount
Pen and ink
5 ½ x 4 ½ inches
Literature: Claudia J Nahson, *The Art of William Steig*,
New York, Yale University Press, 2007, Page 104

180

I'M THE LUCKIEST MAN IN THE WORLD
Signed
Inscribed with title below mount
Pen and ink with elements of collage
5 ½ x 4 ½ inches

181

I'M MARRIED TO THE BEST GODDAM WOMAN THERE IS
Signed
Inscribed with title below mount
Pen and ink
5 ½ x 4 inches
Literature: *The New York Times*, 23 February 1947,
'Marriage – by Wm Steig' by Charles Poore

182
ALBERT IS THE MORE INTROVERT TYPE
Signed
Inscribed with title below mount
Pen and ink
5 ¼ x 4 ¾ inches
Literature: *The New York Times*, 23 February 1947,
'Marriage – by Wm Steig' by Charles Poore

183
SHE HAS SUCH STRANGE MOODS
Signed
Inscribed with title below mount
Pen and ink
5 ½ x 4 ½ inches
Literature: *The New York Times*, 23 February 1947,
'Marriage – by Wm Steig' by Charles Poore

The New Yorker

184
I'M AFRAID IT'S ALL UP HERE, MR PEPPER
Signed
Inscribed 'I'm afraid it's all up here, Mr Botts' below mount
Pen ink and watercolour
6 x 6 ½ inches
Illustrated: *The New Yorker*, 9 June 1956, Page 29

185
JUST A MINUTE. I THINK NANCY WOULD
LIKE TO TALK TO YOU
Signed
Pen ink and watercolour
5 ½ x 4 ½ inches
Illustrated: *The New Yorker*, 12 April 1958, Page 36

186
HONEST, I DON'T HAVE A CENT.
I'M JUST A COLLEGE BOY
Signed
Pen and ink with watercolour
4 ½ x 4 ½ inches
Illustrated: *The New Yorker*, 10 October 1959,
Page 44

187
NOW, I'M NOT GOING TO
HIGH-PRESSURE YOU, MR BOWSER.
WE'LL JUST LET THE FACTS SPEAK
FOR THEMSELVES
Signed
Pen ink and watercolour with bodycolour
4 ¾ x 6 ½ inches
Illustrated: *The New Yorker*, 4 April 1959,
Page 34

LUDWIG BEMELMANS

Ludwig Bemelmans (1898-1962)

Though he has achieved lasting fame as the creator of the hugely popular *Madeline* series of children's books, Ludwig Bemelmans was a wide-ranging and prolific illustrator and cartoonist. His early years serving in hotels in 'Roaring Twenties' Manhattan gave him access to New York high society, and his artwork would later become symbolic of the city's glamour, appearing on covers of *The New Yorker*, in advertisements and painted on the walls of hotel bars.

Ludwig Bemelmans was born in Meran, South Tyrol in Austria-Hungary (now Italy), on 27 April 1898, the son of Lampert Bemelmans, a Belgian painter and hotelier, and his wife, Franciska (née Fischer). Until the age of six, he lived with his parents in Gmunden, on the Traunsee in Upper Austria. In 1904, after his father left his mother and Ludwig's governess, both pregnant with his child, for another woman, Bemelmans moved with his mother and his brother, Oscar, to live in his mother's native city of Regensburg, Germany.

Bemelmans endured a difficult childhood. He had grown up being taught French as his first language, and his struggles with the German language and style of discipline made him an outcast at school. After failing the same year repeatedly, he was sent to boarding school in Rothenburg, Bavaria. He remained a disobedient and defiant student and was expelled. His mother responded by sending him back to Tyrol to be apprenticed to his uncle Hans and aunt Marie, who owned a chain of hotels. Again, he showed himself to be a poor and rebellious worker, and was tried across the various hotels and fired from each. In an interview with *The New York Times* in 1941, he claimed that matters came to head when, in response to a head waiter threatening him with a leather whip, Bemelmans shot him in the abdomen. Though the waiter survived, Bemelmans was given the choice of being sent to reform school or to America.

Bemelmans arrived in America on Christmas Eve 1914, at the age of sixteen. He had expected to be reunited with his father, who had moved to the United States some years earlier to become a jeweller, but he forgot to pick him up, and Bemelmans spent his first Christmas in America on Ellis Island. Through his family's connections, he had arrived in New York with letters of introduction to the managers of several hotels, and found work as a busboy at the Hotel McAlpin and Hotel Astor, before moving to the Ritz Carlton. When the United States entered the First World War in 1917, he enlisted in the US Army. Though his German heritage meant that he was not sent abroad, he spent the war working as an aide in a mental hospital in Buffalo, New York. He wrote about his wartime experiences in

the book *My War with the United States* (1941). In 1918, he became an American citizen and returned to the Ritz Carlton, moving to the banquet department and working his way up to assistant manager. Throughout his time at the hotel, he sketched and drew, on napkins, notepads and menus, often caricaturing his colleagues and guests. After he was encouraged to pursue a career as a cartoonist by a waiter at the hotel, he quit his job in 1926 and was hired by the *New York World* to produce the cartoon series, 'Thrilling Adventures of Count Bric a Brac'. However, the series received complaints and, after six months, he was fired and forced to return to his job at the Ritz Carlton.

In the mid-1920s, Bemelmans had met an English ballet dancer, Rita Pope, and they were married soon after. The marriage was tempestuous and in 1929 their divorce was finalised. The breakup of his marriage forced Bemelmans to re-evaluate his life and, disgusted by what his career was doing to his health and dismayed by his lack of direction, he quit the Ritz Carlton and, in July 1929, moved into a Greenwich Village studio to begin work as a full-time artist. Though the effects of The Great Depression forced him to return once again to the Ritz Carlton just three months later, he remained determined to succeed and began to earn commissions as a freelance artist in an advertising studio, producing work for companies such as General Foods and Jell-O. He suffered more tragedy in his personal life in 1931 when his brother Oscar, who had joined him at the Ritz Carlton in 1922, died when he fell down an elevator shaft at the hotel. The following year, he met May Massee, children's book editor at Viking Press. She encouraged him to start writing books for children and in 1934 he published his first book, *Hansi*, inspired by his own childhood in Austria. The same year, he met and eloped with Madeleine Freund, a former nun and an artist's model. Their honeymoon in Belgium in 1936 inspired his second children's book, *The Golden Basket*, for which he won the John Newbery Medal. Later that year, Madeleine gave birth to the couple's only daughter, Barbara.

In 1938, whilst visiting the Ile d'Yeu off the coast of France with his wife and daughter, Bemelmans was hospitalised when he was knocked off his bike by a lorry. He recalled that in the next room of the hospital 'was a little girl who had her appendix out, and on the ceiling over my bed was a crack that, in the varying light of the morning, night and noon, and evening, looked like a rabbit'. Along with the stories his mother had told him about growing up in a convent school, these experiences inspired the book *Madeline*, which would become his most famous creation. Published in 1939, the book was an instant success and was awarded a Caldecott Medal, it was followed by *Madeline's Rescue* (1953), ☞ *Page 188*

Biography of Ludwig Bemelmans continued from Page 187

for which Bemelmans also won the Caldecott Medal, *Madeline and the Bad Hat* (1956), *Madeline and the Gypsies* (1959) and *Madeline in London* (1961). *Madeline's Christmas*, first appearing as a series in the monthly magazine, *McCall's*, in 1956, was released posthumously in 1985. The story, *Madeline in America and Other Holiday Tales*, was discovered after his death and published in 1999.

Though the *Madeline* series was to be his most famous achievement, Bemelmans continued to work prolifically in a multitude of media. He wrote and published 19 books for children, including *Fifi* (1940) and *A Tale of Two Glimps* (1946), and over 40 books in total. His illustrations appeared regularly in *The New Yorker* (for which he also produced more than 30 covers), *Town and Country*, *Vogue* and *Fortune*. During the Second World War, he travelled to Hollywood and spent a brief period as a screenwriter at MGM, creating the 1945 Fred Astaire film, *Yolanda and the Thief*. He was also in demand as a muralist, creating designs for Hapsburg House, a Viennese restaurant on 55th Street, New York, and, most famously in 1947, the bar at the Carlyle Hotel on the Upper East Side, for which he was paid with a year and a half's free accommodation at the hotel. The mural is still on display and remains the only example of his work on view to the public.

Ludwig Bemelmans died of pancreatic cancer on 1 October 1962 at his apartment in the National Arts Club, 15 Grammercy Park South, at the age of 64. As a former corporal in the US Army, he was buried at Arlington National Cemetery in Virginia. To commemorate the 75th birthday of his creation, Madeline, in 2014, the New York Historical Society held an exhibition entitled 'Madeline in New York: The Art of Ludwig Bemelmans', featuring more than 90 of his original artworks.

Further reading

Ludwig Bemelmans, Hotel Bemelmans, Woodstock NY: Overlook Press, 2002; Jacqueline Fisher Eastman, Ludwig Bemelmans, New York: Twayne Publishers, 1996; Wolf Koepke, John A Garratty & Mark C Carnes (eds), 'Bemelmans, Ludwig 27 April 1898-1 October 1962)', *American National Biography*, New York: Oxford University Press, 1999, https://doi.org/10.1093/anb/9780198606697.article.1600104; John Bemelmans Marciano, *Bemelmans: The Life & Art of Madeline's Creator*, New York: Viking Press, 1999

The biography of Ludwig Bemelmans is written by Alexander Beetles.

ON HOT SUMMER NIGHTS HE GHOSTED
Signed
Pen and ink with watercolour
17 x 13 inches
Similar to Ludwig Bemelmans, *Madeline and the Bad Hat*, New York: Viking Press, 1956, [unpaginated]

DAVID LEVINE
David Julian Levine (1926-2009)

David Levine was widely acknowledged as one of the greatest, and most influential, caricaturists of the second half of the twentieth century. Best known as the staff artist of *The New York Review of Books*, he revived the tradition of American political caricature that originated in the nineteenth century with Thomas Nast, and has been frequently described as equal to Honoré Daumier. However, he sustained an equally distinguished career as a painter, producing figurative oils and watercolours in a poetically naturalistic style. His love of Corot and Vuillard, Eakins and Sargent, pervades his studies of Coney Island and the Garment District. But more fundamental to both his paintings and his caricatures is the fact that he said, 'I love my species'.

For a biography of David Levine, please refer to *The Illustrators*, 2010, pages 277-278.

189
KATHERINE MANSFIELD
Signed and dated 80
Inscribed with title on reverse
Pen and ink, 13 ½ x 10 ½ inches
Provenance: David Levine;
The Sir Christopher Ondaatje Collection of Literary Portraits
Illustrated: *The New York Review of Books*, 15 May 1980, 'Katherine Mansfield's Secrets' by Claire Tomalin (a review of a biography of Mansfield by Antony Alpers)

Katherine Mansfield
Born and brought up in New Zealand, the Modernist writer, Katherine Mansfield (1888-1923), settled in England in 1908, and published her first collection of short stories, *In a German Pension*, in 1911. In that year, she met the writer, John Middleton Murry, who, in 1918, would become her second husband. Together they edited the magazine, *Rhythm* (1912-13) and its short-lived successor, *The Blue Review* (1913), both of which published her work. They also befriended D H Lawrence and his wife Frieda, and, as a result, would become the models for Gudrun and Gerald in Lawrence's *Women in Love* (1920). Mansfield began her most prolific period of writing in 1916, drawing on her New Zealand childhood for some of her finest stories, including 'Prelude', which was published by Leonard and Virginia Woolf's Hogarth Press in 1918. By that time, she had been diagnosed with pulmonary tuberculosis, and her poor health led her to live for long periods abroad, often seeking out unorthodox cures. Nevertheless, she continued to write, and published two mature collections of stories, *Bliss* (1920) and *The Garden Party and Other Stories* (1922). In 1922, she travelled to Fontainebleau with her lover, Ida Baker, and settled at Georges Gurdjieff's Institute for the Harmonious Development of Man, dying there the following year.

Antonin Artaud

190
ANTONIN ARTAUD
Signed and dated 68
Pen and ink
7 x 7 inches
Illustrated: *New York Review of Books*, 29 February 1968, 'Poet of Unreason' by John Weightman (a review of *Artaud Anthology*, edited and translated by Jack Hirschman)

French-born Antonin Artaud (1896-1948) began his career as an actor, both on stage, in the troupe of his teacher, Charles Dullin, at the Théâtre de L'Atelier, Paris, and on screen in such masterpieces of silent cinema as Abel Gance's *Napoleon* (1927) and Carl Theodor Dreyer's *La Passion de Jeanne d'Arc* (1928). In 1926, he founded the Théâtre Alfred-Jarry with Robert Aron and Roger Vitrac, and there staged one of his earliest plays. However, he demonstrated his full power as an experimental director only a decade later, when, in 1935, he staged Shelley's *The Cenci* at the Théâtre des Folies-Wagram. This put into practice his manifestos of a 'Theatre of Cruelty' (1932), which sought to wake an audience from its false sense of reality through a violent assault on its senses, and especially the use of image and sound rather than language. Always physically and mentally fragile, he spent much of his later life in psychiatric hospitals, though continued to write until his death, publishing, among other works, *Le Théâtre et son double* (1938), which includes his manifestos and has proved highly influential on subsequent theatre practitioners, including Samuel Beckett [188] and Peter Brook.

Samuel Beckett

Born into a Protestant family in Ireland, Samuel
Beckett (1906-1989) proved himself a brilliant
scholar in English, French and Italian at Trinity College,
Dublin. Moving to Paris to teach in 1928, he formed
a significant friendship with James Joyce, and took
on his mantle, becoming in time, what some have
considered, the last great Modernist. Settling
permanently in France during the 1930s, he wrote
in both English and French, and often translated his
own work, as well as that of others. He first
established himself as a novelist with *Murphy* (1938),
the trilogy consisting of *Molloy*, *Malone Dies* and
The Unnamable (1951-53), and *Watt* (1953). However,
it is as the writer of the play, *Waiting for Godot*, that
he reached a wider audience and public acclaim,
through productions in Paris (1953) and London
(1955). This led him to be considered – by Martin
Esslin in 1960 – a key figure in the 'Theatre of the
Absurd', a revolutionary body of anti-realist plays
that examined existentialist themes and so influenced
such later playwrights as Harold Pinter and Tom
Stoppard [193]. Though he produced three further
full-length plays – *Endgame* (1957), *Krapp's Last
Tape* (1958) and *Happy Days* (1961) – his work, for
both the stage and the page, became increasingly
minimal. In 1969, he was awarded the Nobel Prize
for Literature, for 'writing, which … in the destitution
of modern man acquires its elevation'. His tragi-comic
outlook is simultaneously despairing and exhilarating.

191
SAMUEL BECKETT
Signed and dated 71
Pen and ink
13 ¾ x 11 inches
Illustrated: *New York Review of Books*, 8 April 1971,
'Original Sin and Dog Biscuits' by Nigel Dennis
(a review of *Collected Works* by Samuel Beckett)

George Orwell

George Orwell was the pen name of Eric Arthur Blair (1903-1950), the writer of some of the most concise and cogent English prose of the twentieth century, which sought to oppose all forms of totalitarianism and champion democratic socialism. In his first full-length work, *Down and Out in Paris and London* (1936), he provided an exposé of poverty based on personal experience of ill-paid jobs. *The Road to Wigan Pier* (1937), published after three novels, extended his investigation into the bleak living conditions of the working classes by surveying the industrial north. *Homage to Catalonia* (1938), provided an account his involvement with the Republican army during the Spanish Civil War, which consolidated his political stance. Though he quickly produced another novel – *Coming Up for Air* (1939) – he would have to wait until the end of the Second World War to publish his two acknowledged masterpieces. *Animal Farm* (1945) is an allegorical novella that satirises the events of Revolutionary and Post-Revolutionary Russia, while *1984* (1949) is a dystopian novel that focusses on one man's hopeless struggle against a totalitarian regime. The present drawing accompanied a review of the collected edition of his many essential shorter works: essays, letters and pieces of journalism.

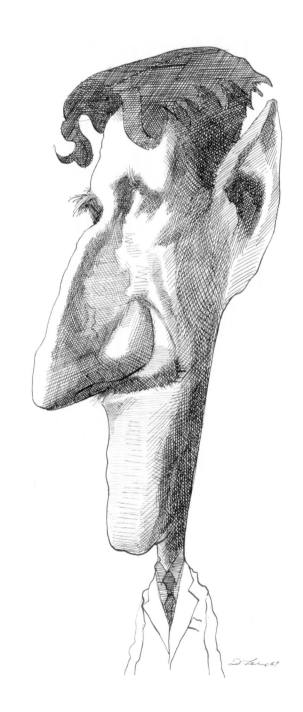

192
GEORGE ORWELL
Signed and dated 69
Inscribed 'Orwell' on reverse
Pen and ink
14 ½ x 9 inches
Illustrated: *The New York Review of Books*, 30 January 1969, 'The Writing on the Wall' by Mary McCarthy (a review of *The Collected Essays, Letters and Journalism of George Orwell*); John Updike (intro), *Pens and Needles. Literary Caricatures by David Levine*, Boston: Gambit, 1969, Page 145; *The New York Review of Books*, 6 November 2003, 'Good Man, Bad World' by John Banville (a review of two books on George Orwell)
Exhibited: 'The Americans Are Coming', Chris Beetles Gallery, May 2015

Brendan Behan

In his short career, the Irish writer, Brendan Behan (1923-1964), achieved great fame. A member of the youth-wing of the Irish Republican Army (IRA) from as young as 14, he served time in both the borstal at Hollesley Bay, Suffolk, and Mountjoy Prison, Dublin. These experiences inspired his play, *The Quare Fellow* (1954), which gained him a wide reputation when produced by Joan Littlewood's Theatre Workshop in London in 1956. He wrote his second play, *The Hostage* (1958), in the Irish language, having become a fluent speaker of it while in prison. Productions of its English-language version ensured international success, which was immediately consolidated by the publication of an autobiographical novel, *Borstal Boy*. However, success led him to play up to the image of him as a wise-cracking drunk, and so damage both his health and the quality of his work. He collapsed at the Harbour Lights Bar in Dublin in March 1964, and died soon after. The present drawing was published four months later as an illustration to a review of two of his slighter works.

193
BRENDAN BEHAN
Signed and dated 64
Inscribed with title and 'N Y R', and dated 1964 on reverse
Pen and ink
4 ¼ x 2 ¼ inches
Illustrated: *New York Review of Books*, 30 July 1964, 'Bee-Keeper'
by Christopher Ricks (a review of *The Scarperer* and *Hold Your Hour
and Have Another* by Brendan Behan);
John Updike (intro), *Pens and Needles. Literary Caricatures by David Levine*,
Boston MA: Gambit, 1969, Page 142

Muriel Spark

Born and educated in Edinburgh, Muriel Spark (1918-2006) lived in Rhodesia following her marriage in 1937. However, in 1940, she came to realise that her husband was a manic depressive capable of violent outbursts, so she left him and temporarily placed their son in a convent school. She returned to Britain in 1944 and, following the end of the Second World War, began to write poetry and literary criticism, becoming the editor of *Poetry Review* (1947-48). In 1954, she converted to Roman Catholicism, which she considered to be a crucial step towards her becoming a novelist. *The Comforters* (1957) was the first of 22 novels, the most significant of which include *Memento Mori* (1959), *The Prime of Miss Jean Brodie* (her best known work, 1961), *The Mandelbaum Gate* (winner of the James Tait Black Memorial Prize, 1965) and *The Driver's Seat* (1970). Most are short and elegant, with touches of perversity and black humour. In 1993, she became a Dame Commander of the Order of the British Empire for her services to literature. From the early 1970s, she lived in the Tuscan village of Oliveto with the artist, Penelope Jardine.

194
MURIEL SPARK
Signed and dated 90
Inscribed with title on reverse
Pen and ink
13 ¾ x 10 ½ inches
Provenance: David Levine;
The Sir Christopher Ondaatje Collection of
Literary Portraits
Illustrated: *The New York Review of Books*,
20 December 1990, 'Sociable Murder' by
Gabriele Annan (a review of Spark's *Symposium*)

Woody Allen

The multi-award winning American filmmaker, Woody Allen (born 1935), began his career in his teens by selling jokes to Broadway writers, and was soon writing scripts for television shows. He also wrote short stories and cartoon captions for *The New Yorker* and other magazines. During the 1960s, he supplemented his writing by performing stand-up comedy, developing the persona of an insecure, intellectual 'nebbish' through a series of monologues. Typically, this was the character that he played when he appeared in own films, the first of which were slapstick comedies, including *Take the Money and Run* (1969) and *Sleeper* (1973). The romantic comedy, *Annie Hall* (1977) proved a major turning point, introducing a new level of seriousness and, in the process, garnering four Academy Awards. This was followed by *Interiors* (1978) and *Manhattan* (1979), which revealed the influence of European art cinema. Allen's films of the 1980s are often considered the most developed of his *oeuvre* and include the romantic comedy fantasy, *The Purple Rose of Cairo* (1985), and the comedy dramas, *Hannah and Her Sisters* (1986, winner of three Academy Awards), and *Crimes and Misdemeanors* (1989). However, Allen himself thinks that the psychological thriller, *Match Point* (2005), which divided opinion, is possibly his best film.

195
WOODY ALLEN
Signed and dated 79
Pen and ink
13 x 10 ¼ inches
Illustrated: *New York Review of Books*, 16 August 1979, 'Letter from "Manhattan"' by Joan Didion (a review of *Manhattan*, *Interiors* and *Annie Hall*)

Tom Stoppard

Tom Stoppard (born 1937) fled his birthplace of Zlin, in Czechoslovakia, in the wake of imminent Nazi occupation, and spent the Second World War in Singapore and India. He settled with his family in Britain in 1946, and took his stepfather's surname. On leaving school, he became a journalist and then a playwright. In 1966, he attracted much attention with his absurdist tragicomedy, *Rosencrantz and Guildenstern Are Dead*, which was influenced by Samuel Beckett's *Waiting for Godot*. This was followed by many other inventive stage plays, including *Travesties* (1974), *Every Good Boy Deserves Favour* (1977, with music by André Previn), *The Real Thing* (1982), *Arcadia* (1993) and *The Invention of Love* (1997). He has also written for television, radio and film, winning an Academy Award for Best Original Screenplay for *Shakespeare in Love* (1998). His work often treats such themes as human rights and political freedom with dazzling wit and a strong sense of theatricality. He was knighted in 1997 and admitted to the Order of Merit in the year 2000.

196
TOM STOPPARD
Signed and dated 95
Inscribed with title on reverse
Pen and ink
13 ¾ x 10 ¾ inches
Provenance: David Levine;
The Sir Christopher Ondaatje Collection
of Literary Portraits
Illustrated: *The New York Review of Books*,
8 June 1995, 'Twice Around the Grounds'
by Anne Barton (a review of
Stoppard's *Arcadia*)

Margaret Atwood

The acclaimed Canadian writer, Margaret Atwood (born 1939), first received recognition as a poet, her first two collections – *Double Persephone* (1961) and *The Circle Game* (1966) – both winning awards. However, while she has continued to write and publish poetry that reflects her essential preoccupations, she soon became better known as a novelist. The first of her 18 novels, *The Edible Woman*, appeared in 1969, and set the tone for subsequent works in its exploration of gender and identity. She established herself as an important voice in Canadian literature with her second novel, *Surfacing*, and her first non-fiction work, *Survival: A Thematic Guide to Canadian Literature* (both 1972). Her reputation was confirmed by the reception of her sixth novel, the speculative dystopian fable, *The Handmaid's Tale* (1985), which won both the Arthur C Clarke Award and the Governor General's Award. As the result of subsequent adaptations, notably the 2017 television series, and a prize-winning sequel, *The Testaments* (2019), this has become her best known work. Other major novels include *Cat's Eye* (1988), *Alias Grace* (1996), *The Blind Assassin* (2000) and *Oryx and Crake* (2003), the last signaling her increasing concern for mankind's effect on the environment. She has also produced children's books, graphic novels and many short stories. Her achievements outside of writing include the invention of the remote signaling device, *LongPen* (2006), while her many honours include the PEN Center USA's Lifetime Achievement Award (2017).

197
MARGARET ATWOOD
Signed and dated 89
Inscribed with title on reverse
Pen and ink
13 ½ x 10 ¾ inches
Provenance: David Levine;
The Sir Christopher Ondaatje Collection of
Literary Portraits
Illustrated: *The New York Review of Books*,
27 April 1989, 'Mystery Women' by Robert
Towers (a review of Atwood's *Cat's Eye* and
novels by Saul Bellow and Susanna Moore)

ARNOLD ROTH
Arnold Roth (born 1929)

'Arnold Roth is surely the most imaginative and humorous graphic artist of this or any other day. Even Max Beerbohm at his best would have to take a back seat.' (George Plimpton, *Paris Review*)

For a biography of Arnold Roth, please refer to *The Illustrators*, 2015, page 158.

198
OUR COTTONTAIL CORNUCOPIA RUNNETH OVER
Signed
Pen ink and watercolour with bodycolour on board
18 x 20 ¾ inches
Illustrated: *VIP: The Playboy Club Magazine: Tenth Anniversary Issue*, Spring 1970

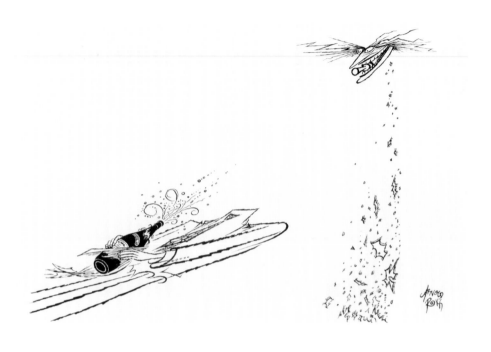

199

REMOVE A CHAMPAGNE CORK
WITH YOUR TEETH
Signed and inscribed with title
Pen and ink
8 ½ x 11 inches
Illustrated: B L Andrews, *Digging Your Own
Grave*, New York: St Martin's Mass Market
Paper, 1996
Exhibited: 'The Americans Are Coming',
Chris Beetles Gallery, May 2015

200

TELL A FEMINIST THAT WHAT SHE
REALLY NEEDS IS A MAN TO SLAP
SOME SENSE INTO HER
Signed
Inscribed with title below mount
Pen and ink
6 ¾ x 9 ½ inches
Illustrated: B L Andrews, *Digging Your Own
Grave*, New York: St Martin's Mass Market
Paper, 1996, Page 6
Exhibited: 'The Americans Are Coming',
Chris Beetles Gallery, May 2015

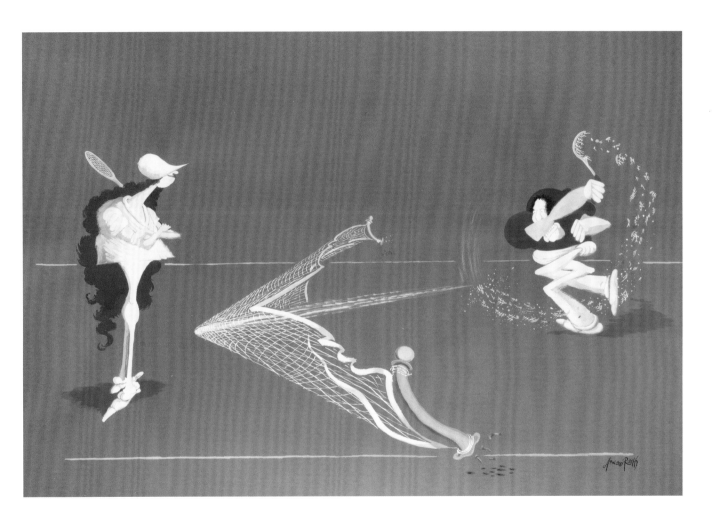

201
THE TENNIS GAME
Signed
Bodycolour with watercolour on tinted paper
18 ½ x 24 ½ inches

ED SOREL

Edward Sorel (born 1929)

Edward Sorel's clever and unforgiving satire is the product of a
lifetime spent observing and criticising the unpleasant reality of
the American Dream. His experiences of recent history from the
Great Depression to Al-Qaeda, and his disdain for the greasy
politics in between, have lent his cartoons a formidable bite that
those his junior rarely match.

For a biography of Ed Sorel, please refer to *The Illustrators*, 2014,
pages 248-250.

202
LITERARY PORTRAITS
(GEORGE ELIOT, MARCEL PROUST, NORMAN MAILER, LEO TOLSTOY,
LILLIAN HELLMAN, BERTOLT BRECHT, CARL JUNG, W B YEATS,
AYN RAND, JEAN-PAUL SARTRE)
Signed
Chalk
18 x 28 ½ inches
Provenance: The Sir Christopher Ondatje Literary Portrait Collection
Illustrated: Edward Sorel, *Literary Lives*, London: Bloomsbury, 2006,
Dust Jacket

14 Contemporaries

MICHAEL FOREMAN

Michael Foreman, RDI (born 1938)

While Michael Foreman is perhaps best known as one of the most outstanding contemporary creators of children's books, he is a wide-ranging artist, illustrating literary classics and working as a painter.

For a biography of Michael Foreman, please refer to *The Illustrators*, 2018, pages 132-133.

Michael Foreman recently illustrated his own *The Mermaid's Christmas Adventure* (Mabecron Books, 2019) and Michael Morpurgo's *Boy Giant: Son of Gulliver* (Harper Collins, 2019). Two further books to his own texts are due to be published: *Happy Times* (Andersen Press) and *Noa and the Little Elephant* (Harper Collins).

In 2017, the Chris Beetles Gallery mounted a major retrospective, 'Michael Foreman: Telling Tales', which was accompanied by a fully-illustrated 140-page catalogue.

Michael Foreman introduces Soggy the Bear

'Philip Moran, author of the *Soggy the Bear* books, was a Master Mariner who sailed the oceans of the world until he retired and returned to his native St Ives and became a fisherman.

Whilst out on one of his fishing trips one day, Phil found a waterlogged teddy bear caught in his nets. He took him home, dried him out and christened him Soggy.

One day, Phil introduced Soggy to me, his long-time friend, and I encouraged him to write the story of the rescue.

A plan was hatched with our friend, Ron Johns (who owns the local bookshop in St Ives, together with several other bookshops in the West Country). Ron liked the story, and I agreed to illustrate it, and so Mabecron Books was born and Ron became the publisher of the Soggy Series.

Such was the success of *Soggy The Bear*, that five more Soggy books have followed in his Soggy paw prints.'

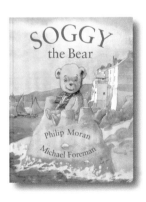

203 (opposite)
SOGGY WOULD LIKE TO TELL THE
LITTLE GIRL HE IS SAFE AND HAPPY
Signed
Watercolour with pencil
8 ¾ x 6 ¾ inches
Illustrated: Philip Moran, *Soggy the Bear*,
Plymouth: Mabecron Books, 2006, [unpaginated]

204
THE LITTLE GIRL BUILT A SANDCASTLE AND PLACED
HER FAVOURITE TEDDY BEAR ON TOP, SO HE COULD
LOOK AT THE ROCKS AND THE BLUE-GREEN SEA
Signed and inscribed with book title
Watercolour with pencil
11 ¼ x 17 ¼ inches
Illustrated: Philip Moran, *Soggy the Bear*,
Plymouth: Mabecron Books, 2006, [unpaginated]

205
'THIS IS THE LIFE', HE THOUGHT. 'I AM KING ON
MY VERY OWN CASTLE.'
Signed and inscribed with book title
Watercolour with pencil
11 ¼ x 17 ¼ inches
Illustrated: Philip Moran, *Soggy the Bear*,
Plymouth: Mabecron Books, 2006, [unpaginated]

206
EVERY WAVE TOOK MORE OF THE SAND BENEATH HIM AND
SLOWLY THE CASTLE BEGAN TO CRUMBLE
Signed and inscribed with book title
Watercolour with bodycolour and pencil
11 ½ × 17 ¼ inches
Illustrated: Philip Moran, *Soggy the Bear*,
Plymouth: Mabecron Books, 2006, [unpaginated]

207
HE SAW THE BLUE AND SILVER FISH DARTING UNDER HIM AS
THEY WENT CRAZY ATTACKING THE COLOURED FEATHERS
ON THE FISHERMEN'S HOOKS
Signed and inscribed with book title
Watercolour with pencil
11 ½ x 17 inches
Illustrated: Philip Moran, *Soggy the Bear*,
Plymouth: Mabecron Books, 2006, [unpaginated]

208
GRABBING THE GAFF HE HOOKED THE LITTLE BEAR BY THE
SCARF AROUND HIS NECK AND HAULED HIM INTO THE BOAT
Signed and inscribed with book title
Watercolour with pencil
11 ¼ x 17 ¼ inches
Illustrated: Philip Moran, *Soggy the Bear*,
Plymouth: Mabecron Books, 2006, [unpaginated]

209

JACK AND HIS GRANDFATHER TOOK
THE LITTLE BEAR HOME AND GAVE HIM
A NICE WARM SOAPY BATH
Signed
Watercolour with pencil
4 ½ x 4 ½ inches
Illustrated: Philip Moran, *Soggy the Bear*,
Plymouth: Mabecron Books, 2006, [unpaginated]

210

THE NOISE THE BEAR HEARD WAS NOT
HIS HEART BUT THE SLOW BEAT OF THE
ENGINE IN THE WATER
Signed and inscribed with book title
Watercolour with bodycolour and pencil
11 ¼ x 17 ¼ inches
Illustrated: Philip Moran, *Soggy the Bear*,
Plymouth: Mabecron Books, 2006, [unpaginated]

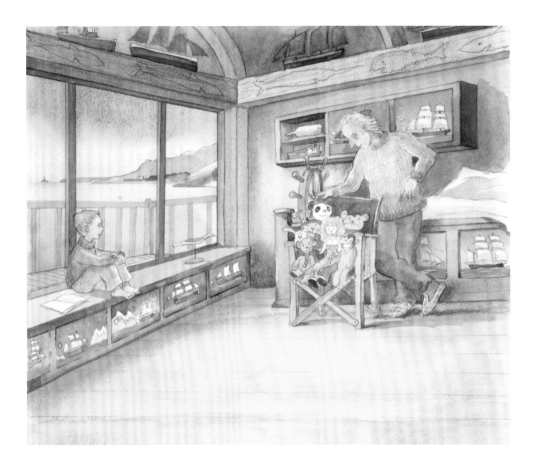

211
THE OLD FISHERMAN CARRIED SOGGY
CAREFULLY UP INTO HIS LIVING ROOM AND
PLACED HIM IN THE RESCUE CHAIR WITH ALL
THE OTHER LITTLE PEOPLE AND CREATURES HE
HAD FOUND AND HELPED OVER THE YEARS
Signed and inscribed with book title
Watercolour with pencil
11 ¼ x 12 ¾ inches
Illustrated: Philip Moran, *Soggy the Bear*,
Plymouth: Mabecron Books, 2006, [unpaginated]

212
THEN THEY PEGGED HIM UP IN THE
BATHROOM BY HIS EARS, WHICH SOGGY
THOUGHT WAS A BIT MUCH, UNTIL HE
HAD DRIED RIGHT THROUGH
Signed
Watercolour with pencil
4 ½ x 4 ½ inches
Illustrated: Philip Moran, *Soggy the Bear*,
Plymouth: Mabecron Books, 2006, [unpaginated]

213
SOGGY NOW GOES WITH JACK'S GRANDFATHER TO SCHOOLS TO HELP HIM TELL CHILDREN
HOW DANGEROUS IT CAN BE IF YOU ARE NOT CAREFUL ON THE BEACH
Signed and inscribed with book title
Watercolour with pencil
11 ½ x 11 ¾ inches
Illustrated: Philip Moran, *Soggy the Bear*, Plymouth: Mabecron Books, 2006, [unpaginated]

214
THUMBELINA
Signed and inscribed with title
Inscribed 'from, Michael Foreman's Classic Fairy Tales. 2005' below mount
Watercolour with pencil
13 ½ x 9 ¾ inches
Illustrated: Michael Foreman (reteller), *Classic Fairy Tales*, London:
Chrysalis Childre''s Books, 2005, Page 173, 'Thumbelina'

215
THE CORN DOLLY
Signed twice, inscribed with title and 'Terry Jones Fairy Tales',
and dated 1981
Coloured inks with pencil
12 ¾ x 9 ½ inches
Illustrated: Terry Jones, *Fairy Tales*, London: Pavilion Books, 1981,
Page 10, 'The Corn Dolly'

216
THE KEY
Signed twice, inscribed with title and 'Terry Jones Fairy Tales', and dated 81
Coloured inks with pencil
13 x 9 ¾ inches
Illustrated: Terry Jones, *Fairy Tales*, London: Pavilion Books, 1981,
Page 100, 'The Key'

217
FAR AWAY CASTLE
Signed twice, inscribed with title and dated 81
Inscribed 'Terry Jones Fairy Tales' below mount
Coloured inks with pencil
11 ¾ x 9 ½ inches
Illustrated: Terry Jones, *Fairy Tales*, London: Pavilion Books, 1981,
Page 117, 'Far-Away Castle'

218
CAROL SINGERS
Signed, inscribed with title and
dated '99
Watercolour with bodycolour
and pencil
10 ¼ x 8 inches
Illustrated: Michael Foreman (ed),
*Michael Foreman's Christmas
Treasury*, London: Pavilion
Children's Books, 1999, Page 41,
'Carols in Gloucestershire'

219
WINTER MORNING
Signed and inscribed with title
Sketch of boy on reverse
Watercolour and pencil
9 ½ x 6 ½ inches
Illustrated: Michael Foreman (ed), *Michael Foreman's Christmas Treasury*, London: Pavilion Children's Books, 1999, Page 53, 'Winter Morning'

220
THE DECORATED FOREST
Signed, inscribed with title and dated 1999
Watercolour with bodycolour and pencil
11 x 8 ½ inches
Illustrated: Michael Foreman (ed), *Michael Foreman's Christmas Treasury*, London: Pavilion Children's Books, 1999, Page 51, 'The Decorated Forest'

221
MERRY CHRISTMAS TO ALL AND TO ALL A GOOD NIGHT!
Signed and inscribed with title
Watercolour with bodycolour and pencil
6 ½ x 8 ½ inches
Illustrated: Michael Foreman (ed), *Michael Foreman's Christmas Treasury*,
London: Pavilion Children's Books, 1999, Page 73, 'The Night Before Christmas'

222
THREE SHIPS. ST IVES
Signed and inscribed with title
Watercolour with bodycolour
7 ¼ x 5 ¼ inches
Illustrated: Michael Foreman (ed),
*Michael Foreman's Christmas
Treasury*, London: Pavilion
Children's Books, 1999, Page 122

ALAN LEE
Alan John Lee (born 1947)

Alan Lee is one of the foremost illustrators of myth and fantasy working today. Establishing his interests and his meticulous approach while still a student, he has carried the great British tradition of gift book illustration into the present, introducing it to a new audience. He has done this through both his own drawings and his designs for the phenomenally successful film versions of J R R Tolkien's *The Lord of the Rings* and *The Hobbit*. His many awards include an Academy Award for the Best Art Direction for *The Lord of the Rings: The Return of the King*.

For a biography of Alan Lee, please refer to *The Illustrators*, 2017, page 75.

223
PEREDUR
Signed on back label on backboard
Watercolour
12 ½ x 11 ¾ inches
Illustrated: *The Mabinogion*,
Hendrik-Ido-Ambacht, The Netherlands:
Dragon's Dream, 1982, Page 198,
'The Proud One of the Clearing'

Peredur

Peredur is the Perceval of the Arthurian legends, and the Parsifal of Wagner's opera of that name, famous for his involvement in the quest for the Holy Grail. *The Mabinogion*, in which he appears, is a collection of mediaeval Welsh manuscripts, mostly of the fourteenth century. First translated by Lady Charlotte Guest, and published between 1838 and 1849, it comprises potent national mythology, including some early versions of Arthurian stories.

PETER CROSS

Peter Cross (born 1951)

From 1975, Peter Cross began to emerge as an illustrator of great originality, making his name with books that continue to delight children and adults alike. Unwilling to restrict his fertile imagination to two dimensions, he also created a series of eccentric cabinets of curiosities. Such richness and variety were then directed towards advertising and, in particular, to delightful work for the company, Wine Rack. Cross's dry, yet charming visual-verbal wit has reached a wide international public through designs for greetings cards, first for Gordon Fraser (Hallmark 1995-2000) and then for The Great British Card Company.

For a biography, please refer to *The Illustrators*, 2018, Page 150.

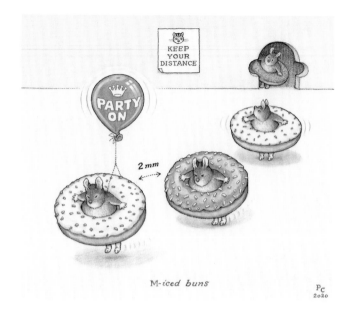

M-*iced buns*

PC
2020

224
A WARM GLOW
Signed with initials
Pen ink and watercolour
8 ½ x 6 ½ inches
Illustrated: Design for a greetings
card for Hallmark

225
M-ICED BUNS
Signed with initials, inscribed
with title and dated 2020
Pen ink and watercolour
8 x 10 inches

227
TOASTIE TOES
Signed with initials and
inscribed with title
Pen ink and watercolour
5 x 4 ½ inches
Illustrated: Design for a greetings
card for Hallmark

229
A PRESENT EXCHANGE
Signed with initials
Watercolour and pencil
4 x 4 inches
Illustrated: Design for a greetings card for Hallmark

228
CHRISTMAS NIGHT
Signed with initials
Watercolour with bodycolour
9 x 13 ¼ inches

226 (opposite)
ZOOMING
Signed with initials and
dated 2020
Pen ink and watercolour
3 ¾ x 4 ¼ inches

SARA MIDDA
Sara Midda (born 1951)

Sara Midda has gained an international reputation for her illustrated books and her product designs. While her work is often enchantingly diminutive in scale, it ranges in character from delicate, jewel-like watercolours to sharply humorous, even surreal, pen and ink drawings. Handwritten words combine actively with the images, whether as speech emitting from the mouths of ever characterful figures or in longer texts. If humans and animals are revealed at both their most vulnerable and their most endearing, the world that they inhabit is essentially edenic, a veritable garden of delights.

For a biography of Sara Midda, please refer to *The Illustrators*, 2016, pages 118-119.

Nos **230-233** were all drawn for an American television listings magazine, circa 1970s

230
THE QUEEN AND HER SCEPTRE
Signed
Pen and ink
4 x 2 ½ inches

231
THE PAGEANT LINEUP
Signed
Pen and ink
2 ¾ x 3 ¼ inches

232
THE QUEEN ON HER LITTER
Signed
Pen and ink
2 ¼ x 3 ¾ inches

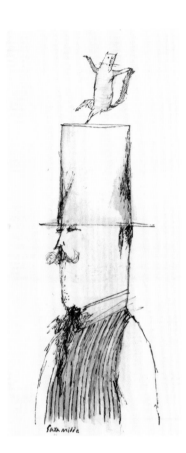

233
THE CORONATION
Signed, Pen and ink, 2 ½ x 2 inches

234
THE HOLLYWOOD HAT
Signed
Pen and ink
3 ¼ x 3 inches
Illustrated: *The New York Times*

235
THE CAT DANCING
ON MY HAT
Signed
Pen and ink with watercolour
4 ¼ x 2 inches

236
TAKING THE CATS FOR A WALK
Signed
Pen and ink with watercolour
4 ½ x 6 ¼ inches

Nos **237-246** are all illustrated in
Sara Midda, *In and Out of the Garden*,
New York: Workman Publishing,
1981, [unpaginated]

237 (above right)
DAYS OF RIPENED FRUIT,
WHERE BERRIES HUNG IN
CLUSTERS AND THE
FORBIDDEN PLUM PROVED
TOO TEMPTING
Signed
Pen ink and watercolour
4 x 3 inches

238
YOU WHO EMPLOY YOUR TIME
TO CULTIVATE YOUR GARDENS,
AND TO MAKE THEIR
GLORY GREAT
Signed
Pen ink and watercolour
4 x 1 ¾ inches

239 (below right)
CUSTOMS OF LOVE
Signed
Pen ink and watercolour
4 x 4 inches

240
ESPALIERS
Signed
Watercolour with pencil
2 ¾ x 3 ¼ inches

241
TOPIARY
Signed
Pen and ink with pencil
5 ¼ x 4 ¼ inches

242
CHAMOMILE
Signed
Watercolour with pen and ink
3 ¾ x 3 ¼ inches

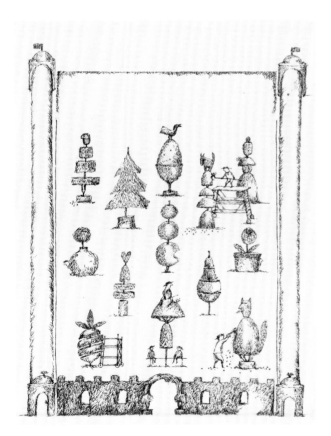

243
MAKE A LITTLE SQUARE OR
ROUND HOLE IN A TREE OR IN
SOME GREAT ARME THEREOF
Signed
Pen ink and watercolour
5 ½ x 4 inches

244
THE PLEASURES OF AN ORCHARD
Signed
Pen ink and watercolour
4 x 3 ¼ inches

The illustrations on the right read:

THE APPLE.
·PYRUS MALUS

"in most mens houses of account, where, if
there grow any rare or excellent fruit, it
is then set forth to be seene and tasted."

A Most Favourite Fruit

"FOR PIES, tarts, puddings, sweets, sauces
· · · · · ONE third of boiled apple pulp, baked
with two thirds of flour, having been properly
fermented with yeast for twelve hours, makes
a very excellent bread, and extremely light
and palatable.
· · · · · THE fermented juice forms cider.
IN CONFECTIONARY it is used for
comfits, marmalades, jellies and pastes.
IN DYEING, the bark produces a yellow
colour.
THE WOOD is firm, hard, and compact;
hence used for turning." Mr. Elliman.

245
FAR BELOW WHERE EARTH
WORMS TOIL, RADISHES,
JEWEL OF THE UNDERWORLD,
ARE QUICKLY SWELLING
Signed
Pen ink and watercolour
5 x 3 ½ inches

246
THE APPLE
Signed
Pen ink and watercolour
5 ¼ x 3 inches

Nos **247-262** are all designs for stationery for Mitsukoshi, a Japanese
chain of department stores

248
THE DOG WITH THE CHRISTMAS TREE TAIL
Signed
Pen ink and watercolour
1 ¼ x 1 ¾ inches

247
AN EXCHANGE OF BONES
Signed
Pen ink and watercolour
2 ½ x 4 inches

249
MY BEST FRIEND
Signed and inscribed
with title
Pen ink and watercolour
1 ½ x 3 inches

250 (below)
SHOES FOR CATS
Signed
Pen ink and watercolour
1 x 2 inches

251 (below right)
EXCHANGING GIFTS
Signed
Pen ink and watercolour
1 x 2 ¼ inches

252
THE CANDLESTICK CAT
Signed
Pen ink and watercolour
2 ½ x 2 ¼ inches

253
A DOG FOR THE WINTER
(COMES EQUIPPED AS HOT
WATER BOTTLE)
Signed
Pen and ink with watercolour
3 x 3 ½ inches

254
THE DOG WITH THE
CANDLE TAIL
Signed
Pen ink and watercolour
1 ½ x 1 ¾ inches

255
FOR YOU
Signed
Pen ink and watercolour
1 ¼ x 2 inches

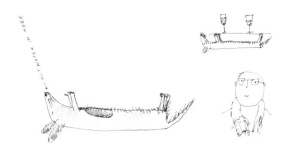

256
A GAME OF CAT AND MOUSE
Signed
Pen ink and watercolour
1 x 3 ¾ inches

257
WHAT COULD IT BE?
Signed
Pen ink and watercolour
2 ¼ x 1 ¾ inches

258
THE CAT GOLDFISH BOW
SignedL
Pen ink and watercolour
2 ¾ x 2 ½ inches

259
THANK YOU ...
Signed
Pen ink and watercolour
4 ¼ x 2 ¾ inches

260
MY CARROT CAKE
Signed
Pen ink and watercolour
2 x 2 inches

261
FROM ME
Signed
Pen ink and watercolour
1 ¼ x 1 ½ inches

262
THE PET RHINOCEROS
Signed
Pen ink and watercolour
2 ¼ x 4 inches

SIMON DREW
Simon Brooksby Drew (born 1952)

Simon Drew has combined his zoological training, his skill as a draughtsman, and his inventive approach to languages to create a unique and highly popular comic art.

For a biography of Simon Drew, please refer to *The Illustrators*, 2018, Page 157.

Nos **263-269** are all designs for Greetings Cards

For each of the last eight years, Simon Drew has produced the 'Spot Puzzle' in the Christmas issue of *The Spectator*. This year, he produced the double page 'Lockdown Conundrum' for the *Daily Mail* and two more for *The Spectator*.

263
THE HOUND OF MUSIC
Signed and inscribed with title
Pen ink and coloured pencil
7 ½ x 6 inches
Illustrated: *Famous Phrases*, Simon Drew's Calendar 2021, March

264
HIPPO CAMPERS
Signed and inscribed with title
Pen ink and coloured pencil
4 ¾ x 6 inches

the hound of music

Hippo Campers

265
MUSICAL MEDICINES
Signed and inscribed with title
Pen ink and coloured pencil
7 ½ x 11 inches

GROUP PUG

CAT·O·PILLARS

266
GROUP PUG
Signed and inscribed with title
Pen ink and coloured pencil
7 x 5 ½ inches

267
CAT-O-PILLARS
Signed and inscribed with title
Pen ink and coloured pencil
7 ½ x 6 inches

PINK FREUD

we buy any cat.com

268
PINK FREUD
Signed and inscribed with title
Pen ink and coloured pencil
7 ¼ x 5 ½ inches
Illustrated: *Famous Phrases*, Simon Drew's Calendar 2021, July

269
WE BUY ANY CAT.COM
Signed and inscribed with title
Pen ink and coloured pencil
7 ½ x 6 inches

AMANDA HALL

Amanda Hall (born 1956)

Amanda Hall is an award-winning contemporary illustrator, particularly renowned for her wonderfully decorative and colourful children's book illustrations, as well as her work for educational publications both in Britain and America.

For a biography of Amanda Hall, please refer to *The Illustrators*, 2011, page 356.

During 2020, Amanda has been busy adding the final touches to her new e-commerce website www.amandahall-illustration.com, which is to be launched shortly. To hear news and updates about Amanda's work, people will be welcome to join her mailing list via her new website contact page.

Amanda is currently illustrating Jennifer Berne's *How the Sea Came to Be* for Eerdmans Books for Young Readers, which will be published in 2022. She is also looking forward to publication by Wisdom Tales in early 2022 of her book *Little Bear*. Little Bear is Amanda's second collaboration with children's author Dawn Casey (following *Babushka* in 2015).

Amanda's books have sold over 500,000 copies worldwide.

Nos **270-276** are all illustrated in Jamila Gavin, *Tales from India*, London: Templar Publishing, 2011

270
SO MANU WENT ALL OVER THE WORLD
Signed
Watercolour, ink and bodycolour
14 x 24 inches
Illustrated: Pages 30-31, 'Manu, the Fish and the Flood'

271
THE MOUNTAIN
CHURNED THE SEA
Signed
Watercolour, ink and bodycolour
12 x 9 ½ inches
Illustrated: Page 13,
'How the World Began'

272
A BEAUTIFUL WHITE HORSE WAS TO BE SET FREE
Signed
Watercolour, ink and bodycolour
10 x 10 inches
Illustrated: Pages 34-35, 'How the River Ganga Came to Earth'

273
THEY MADE THEIR WAY THROUGH THE FOREST
Signed
Watercolour, ink and bodycolour
5 ¼ x 10 inches
Illustrated: Page 65, 'Hanuman, the Greatest'

274
NOBEL PRINCESS,
I COME FROM RAMA
Signed
Watercolour, ink
and bodycolour
12 x 11 ¼ inches
Illustrated: Page 62,
'Hanuman, the Greatest'

275
WHO IS THIS MYSTERIOUS WARRIOR
Signed
Watercolour, ink and bodycolour
7 ¼ x 8 inches
Illustrated: Page 80, 'The Battle of Eighteen Days'

276 (opposite)
ARJUNA LET FLY HIS ARROW
Signed
Watercolour, ink and bodycolour
12 ¼ x 12 ¼ inches
Illustrated: Page 85, 'The Battle of Eighteen Days'

ED MCLACHLAN
Edward Rolland Mclachlan (born 1940)

Ed McLachlan's cartoons offer a comical but often cutting commentary on modern life. From his gormless, baggy-suited businessmen to his ungainly bucktoothed women, his undeniably British sense of humour makes him a master of the macabre with an eye for the ridiculous. In every cleverly observed image, he takes the mundane and delivers the hilariously absurd.

For a biography of Ed Mclachlan, please refer to *The Illustrators*, 2002, page 110.

277
MY HUSBAND ALWAYS SAYS IF YOU WANT A GOOD JOB DOING, THEN DO IT YOURSELF
Signed, inscribed with title and dated 2020
Pen and ink with watercolour
10 x 14 ½ inches
Illustrated: Redraw of a cartoon which originally appeared in *Punch*

"My husband always says if you want a good job doing, then do it yourself."

278

A CAT HAS BEEN DIAGNOSED
WITH CORONAVIRUS
Signed, inscribed with title and dated 12/9/20
Pen ink and watercolour
8 ¾ x 11 ¾ inches

279

NOW IF YOU SEE THE PERSON WHO
ROBBED YOU, POINT HIM OUT
Signed, inscribed with title and dated 6/8/20
Pen and ink with watercolour
6 ½ x 14 ½ inches
Illustrated: Redraw of a cartoon that originally
appeared in *Private Eye*, 9 October 2020, Page 25

– A CAT HAS BEEN DIAGNOSED WITH CORONAVIRUS –

"Now if you can see the person who robbed you, point him out."

"As you can see, folks, there was once a strong English influence here on Easter Island many years ago."

280
AS YOU CAN SEE, FOLKS, THERE WAS ONCE A STRONG ENGLISH INFLUENCE HERE ON EASTER ISLAND MANY YEARS AGO
Signed and inscribed with title
Pen ink and watercolour
12 ½ x 9 ¼ inches
Illustrated: The Oldie, May 2020, Arts Section

"I wish I hadn't ordered the swordfish kebabs."

281
I WISH I HADN'T ORDERED THE
SWORDFISH KEBABS
Signed and inscribed with title
Pen ink and watercolour with bodycolour
9 ½ x 14 inches
Illustrated: *Private Eye*, 31 July 2020, Page 38

-COVID & GOLIATH-

282
COVID & GOLIATH
Signed and inscribed with title
Pen ink and watercolour
12 ½ x 15 inches

"The doctor was so worried about my physical state, he took me off statins and put me on Putins instead."

283
THE DOCTOR WAS SO
WORRIED ABOUT MY
PHYSICAL STATE, HE TOOK
ME OFF STATINS AND PUT
ME ON PUTINS INSTEAD
Signed and inscribed with title
Pen and ink with watercolour
9 ¼ x 11 inches
Illustrated: *Salisbury Review*

"I just can't believe some of the stuff people put down their toilets."

284
I JUST CAN'T BELIEVE SOME
OF THE STUFF PEOPLE PUT
DOWN THEIR TOILETS
Signed and inscribed with title
Pen ink and watercolour
9 ¼ x 14 ¾ inches
Illustrated: *Private Eye*

PETER BROOKES

Peter Derek Brookes, CBE FRSA RDI
(born 1943)

Peter Brookes maintains the most
consistently high standard of any editorial
cartoonist working in Britain today.
His daily political cartoons and regular
'Nature Notes', produced for *The Times*,
are always inventive, incisive and
confidently drawn. They are the fruit of
wide experience as a cartoonist and
illustrator, and of complete independence
from editorial intrusion.

For a biography of Peter Brookes, please refer
to *The Illustrators*, 2009, page 164.

285
AMERICA'S SHAME
Signed and dated '1 x 20'
Pen ink and watercolour
7 ¾ x 10 ¾ inches
Illustrated: *The Times*, 1 October 2020

286
I'M ALL FOR FACEMASKS ... MAKES ME
LOOK LIKE THE LONE RANGER!
Signed and dated '3 vii 20'
Pen ink and watercolour
8 x 11 inches
Illustrated: *The Times*, 3 July 2020

287
OH, DO BE PATIENT, PHILIP! ONE
HAS TO USE WHAT PROTECTION
ONE'S GOT!
Signed and dated '18 iv 20'
Pen ink and watercolour
7 ½ x 10 ¾ inches
Illustrated: *The Times*, 18 April 2020

288
TESTING ISN'T WORKING
Signed, inscribed 'After the Saatchi &
Saatchi Tory Ad', and dated '17 ix 20'
Pen ink and watercolour
7 ½ x 10 ¾ inches
Illustrated: *The Times*, 17 September 2020

289
MANY OF YOU ARE OFFENDED BY
MONUMENTS TO THE PAST ...
Signed dated '12 vi 20'
Pen ink and watercolour
7 ¾ x 10 ¾ inches
Illustrated: *The Times*, 12 June 2020

290
I BELIEVE IN ONE COUNTRY,
TWO SYSTEMS ...
Signed and dated '23 v 20'
Pen ink and watercolour
7 ½ x 10 ¾ inches
Illustrated: *The Times*, 23 May 2020

MATT

Matthew Pritchett, MBE (born 1964), known as 'Matt'

'His genius lies in being witty without being nasty'

(Charles Moore, quoted in Max Davidson, *Daily Telegraph*, 17 October 2008)

Matt's much-loved pocket cartoons for the *Daily Telegraph* provide a consistently original take on the big news stories of the day.

For a biography of the day, please refer to *The Illustrators*, 2009, page 185.

Nos **291-301** are all signed, inscribed with title, drawn in pen ink and watercolour, and illustrated in the *Daily Telegraph*

Matt was awarded Cartoonist of the Year in the Society of Editors' National Press Awards for 2019.

291

THESE COVID RESTRICTIONS ARE INFURIATING.
I JUST WANT TO BE ABLE TO HAVE A BREXIT ROW
WITH MY GRANDCHILDREN
4 x 3 ½ inches
Illustrated: Wednesday 9 September 2020

'The frustrations, isolation and spirit of the protected elderly was never better expressed.'

292

AND THIS IS THE BENCH
DOMINIC CUMMINGS SAT ON
4 x 3 ½ inches
Illustrated: *Daily Telegraph*, Friday 29 May 2020;
The Best of Matt 2020, London: Seven Dials, 2020;
Telegraph Magazine, 10 October 2020, 'Matt picks his 15 favourite cartoons of 2020'

In Matt's words, 'Of course, Dominic Cummings. When everyone is making jokes it is difficult to find one. But I thought about Barnard Castle, and how now the most famous thing about it isn't the ruins any more. It's probably the fact that Dominic Cummings went there.'

Chris Beetles provides a commentary on this year's selection of cartoons by Matt

293
LABOUR
FOR THE MANY BREXIT POSITIONS
NOT THE FEW
4 x 3 ½ inches
Illustrated: *Daily Telegraph*, Thursday
19 September 2019;
The Best of Matt 2020, London:
Seven Dials, 2020

'Matt's parody of the Labour Party nostrum
"For the many, not the few" suggests that
of more interest to the electorate was its
indecisive position on Brexit, which would
harm its chances in the General Election
three months later on 12 December 2019.'

294
THIS MUST BE THE PLACE …
4 x 2 ¾ inches
Illustrated: Saturday 29 September 2018

'As Conservative Party members started
their annual conference in Birmingham,
they would recall the disaster the year
before, on 4 October 2017, when Theresa
May coughed her way through her
keynote speech while letters fell off the
board behind the podium – a metaphor
for a failing Prime Minister in dissolution.'

295
THE OBAMAS HAVE REMOVED ALL
THE HAIR DRYERS
4 x 2 ¾ inches
Illustrated: Sunday 22 January 2017

'Donald Trump succeeded Barack Obama
and took office as the 45th President of the
United States on 20 January 2017, bringing
his hair with him, and so ensuring four
years of memorable responses from the
cartoon community.'

296
I'M EXPECTING A SURPRISE LEAVE,
FOLLOWED BY A CALL FOR UNITY
4 x 2 ¾ inches
Illustrated: Sunday 26 June 2016

*'The unexpected result in the EU Referendum
– three days before this cartoon was published
– divided the nation as 52% voted to leave.
Matt's comedic ability to conflate two major
but unrelated events is combined with a
spooky prescience as England was surprisingly
knocked out of the European Football
Championships a day later by Iceland,
losing 2-1.'*

297
CHEER UP, LUV, THE SEXIST
OBJECTIFYING OF WOMEN IS
COMING TO AN END
3 ½ x 2 ¾ inches
Illustrated: Wednesday 21 January 2015

*'The tabloid newspaper, The Sun, started
showing naked models on "Page 3" in
1969. This controversial but popular
tradition continued until March 2017
when it was considered to be an outdated
fashion. Here Matt has even persuaded a
scaffolder to eschew his leery wolf whistles
in favour of a more considered assessment
of the Gender Debate.'*

298
PLEASE TELL ME HE DIDN'T TRY
TO EAT A YORKSHIRE PUDDING
3 ¾ x 3 ¾ inches
Illustrated: Wednesday 2 July 2014,
Inside cartoon

*'Ed Miliband's elegant relationship
with a bacon sandwich went before him
... all the way to the General Election
on 7 May 2015, which he lost to
David Cameron.'*

299
HAVE YOU NOTICED HOW
MUCH BETTER THE WEATHER WAS
BACK THEN?
4 x 3 ½ inches
Illustrated: Sunday 14 April 2013

*Margaret Thatcher, the Prime Minister of
the United Kingdom from 1979 to 1990,
died on 8 April 2013. There followed a slew
of memorial documentaries and some very
bad weather.'*

300
I'M AFRAID THE FLU VACCINE IS
RESERVED FOR ESSENTIAL PEOPLE –
DUSTBIN MEN
5 x 4 inches
Illustrated: Thursday 6 January 2011

*'Matt's crystal ball is in use again as we
now experience, ten years on, that the
problems of key workers and the allocation
of vital resources have not gone away.'*

301
I'LL DRIVE YOU TO CALAIS ON
CONDITION THAT YOU DON'T TALK
ABOUT NICK CLEGG
5 x 4 inches
Illustrated: Wednesday 21 April 2010

*'Volcanic eruptions in Iceland in April 2010
halted air flights across Europe forcing
desperate plans on to travellers. Matt can
never be enticed to publicly state his personal
views ("I am too shallow to have political
opinions") but his puzzlement over the
Liberal Party is summed up by his enduring
admiration for Nick Clegg. The result of the
General Election on the 6 May was a hung
Parliament producing a coalition government
of the Conservatives and the Liberals.'*

SELECT BIBLIOGRAPHY

Backemeyer 2005
Sylvia Backemeyer (ed), *Picture This: The Artist as Illustrator*,
London: Herbert Press, 2005

Baker 2002
Martin Baker, *Artists of Radio Times. A Golden Age of British Illustration*,
Oxford: The Ashmolean Press & Chris Beetles Ltd, 2002

Bryant 2000
Mark Bryant, *Dictionary of Twentieth-Century British Cartoonists and Caricaturists*, London: Ashgate, 2000

Bryant and Heneage 1994
Mark Bryant and Simon Heneage, *Dictionary of British Cartoonists and Caricaturists 1730-1980*, Aldershot: Scolar Press, 1994

Clark 1998
Alan Clark, *Dictionary of British Comic Artists, Writer and Editors*,
London: The British Library, 1998

Driver 1981
David Driver (compiler), *The Art of Radio Times. The First Sixty Years*,
London: BBC, 1981

Feaver 1981
William Feaver, *Masters of Caricature. From Hogarth and Gillray to Scarfe and Levine*, London: Weidenfeld and Nicolson, 1981

Horne 1994
Alan Horne, *The Dictionary of 20th Century Book Illustrators*,
Woodbridge: Antique Collectors' Club, 1994

Houfe 1996
Simon Houfe, *The Dictionary of British Book Illustrators and Caricaturists 1800-1914*, Woodbridge: Antique Collectors' Club, 1996
(revised edition)

Johnson and Gruetzner
Jane Johnson and Anna Gruetzner, *The Dictionary of British Artists, 1880-1940*, Woodbridge: Antique Collectors' Club, 1986 (reprint)

Khoury 2004
George Khoury (ed), *True Brit. A Celebration of the Great Comic Book Artists of the UK*, Raleigh, NC: TwoMorrows Publishing, 2004

Lewis 1967
John Lewis, *The 20th Century Book*, London: Herbert Press, 1967

Mallalieu 1976
Huon Mallalieu, *The Dictionary of British Watercolour Artists up to 1920*,
Woodbridge: Antique Collectors' Club, 1976

Martin 1989
Douglas Martin, *The Telling Line. Essays on fifteen contemporary book illustrators*, London: Julia MacRae Books, 1989

Matthew and Harrison 2004
H C G Matthew and Brian Harrison (eds), *Oxford Dictionary of National Biography*, Oxford University Press, 2004 (61 vols)

Peppin and Mickelthwait 1983
Brigid Peppin and Lucy Mickelthwait, *The Dictionary of British Book Illustrators: The Twentieth Century*, London: John Murray, 1983

Price 1957
R G G Price, *A History of Punch*, London: Collins, 1957

Ray 1976
Gordon Norton Ray, *The Illustrator and the Book in England from 1790 to 1914*, New York: Pierpoint Morgan Library, 1976

Reid 1928
Forrest Reid, *Illustrators of the Sixties*, London: Faber & Gwyer, 1928

Souter 2007
Nick and Tessa Souter, *The Illustration Handbook. A Guide to the World's Greatest Illustrators*, Royston: Eagle Editions, 2007

Spalding 1990
Frances Spalding, *20th Century Painters and Sculptors*,
Woodbridge: Antique Collectors' Club, 1990

Spielmann 1895
M H Spielmann, *The History of 'Punch'*, London: Cassell and Company, 1895

Suriano 2000
Gregory R Suriano, *The Pre-Raphaelite Illustrators*, New Castle:
Oak Knoll Press/London: The British Library, 2000

Turner 1996
Jane Turner (ed), *The Dictionary of Art*, London: Macmillan, 1996 (34 vols)

Wood 1995
Christopher Wood, *The Dictionary of Victorian Painting*,
Woodbridge: Antique Collectors' Club, 1995 (2 vols)

CUMULATIVE INDEX OF CATALOGUES (1991-2020)

INDEX

(Detail of **114**)